NUMERACY

KEY STAGE 1: YEAR 1/ PRIMARY 2

SUE ATKINSON

Contents

Published by Hopscotch Educational Publishing Ltd,
Althorpe House, Althorpe Street, Leamington Spa CV31 2AU.

© 1999 Hopscotch Educational Publishing

Written by Sue Atkinson
Series design by Blade Communications
Illustrated by Sarah Dempsey
Cover illustration by Claire Boyce
Printed by Clintplan, Southam

Sue Atkinson hereby asserts her moral right to be identified as the author of this work in accordance with the Copyright, Designs and Patents Act, 1988.

ISBN 1-902239-31-8

Introduction

◆ ABOUT THE SERIES ◆

Developing Numeracy Skills is a series of books aimed at developing the basic skills of the 'Framework for teaching mathematics'. There is one book for each year from Reception (Scottish Primary 1), through Key Stage 1 to the end of Key Stage 2 (Scottish Primary 7).

The series offers a structured approach which provides detailed lesson plans to teach specific numeracy skills. A unique feature of the series is the provision of differentiated photocopiable activities which are aimed at considerably reducing teacher preparation time.

◆ ABOUT THIS BOOK ◆

This book is for teachers of Year 1 children and Scottish level P2. It aims to:

◆ give emphasis to those aspects of numeracy that teachers on the National Numeracy Project found to be crucial to raising the standards of numeracy in their classrooms;

◆ support a threefold structured lesson for maximising learning to raise standards;

◆ support teachers in developing children's flexible methods of calculating;

◆ encourage a wide range of mathematical vocabulary by giving some key questions to ask;

◆ support teachers with a wide range of mental maths questions to develop good mental recall with children.

Throughout the book, ocean creatures are used to set maths in a context, but you can adapt the lessons by using your own topic.

(You will find that the contents of the Reception/P1 and the Y2/P3 books in this series are structured in a similar way to assist you if you have a mixed-age class.)

◆ CHAPTER CONTENT ◆

◆ Overall learning objectives

Each chapter has two lesson plans and the overall learning objectives outline the aims for both lessons and the further activities in each chapter.

◆ Assessment focus

This sets out the specific learning objective that you will be able to assess for each individual lesson within the chapter. (See page 4 for more on assessment.)

◆ Resources

This is a list of what you will need to do the lessons.

◆ Oral work and mental calculation

This section is a 'mental maths warm-up' and can have a different learning objective from the main lesson plan. It gives you ideas for how to develop quick mental recall with your children, so keeping key ideas ticking over and giving children the extra practice they need to be confident with mental maths. You can 'mix and match' these to suit your lesson. This section of the lesson would be about 5 or 10 minutes long.

◆ Starting point: whole class

This provides ideas for introducing the activity, and may include key questions to ask the children, so that they can move on to their group task having learned concepts and the vocabulary they will need for the group activities. This starting point is usually about 10 minutes long, depending on the task.

◆ Group activities

This explains the tasks that the children will do. The focus group works with you and this group alternates between different ability groups. The section on teacher-independent groups gives three tasks that can be done more or less independently of you. Sometimes you might only use two of the three independent tasks because one group is the focus group. The Group 1 tasks are the easiest and the Group 3 tasks the hardest. For Year 1/P2 children, this section is only 10 or 15 minutes long, depending on the task. Of course, with young children, many of these tasks need to be structured play, or maths games, and some children will find it hard to stick at our task for the whole lesson, but they will get better as the year goes on.

You need, therefore, to use the generic sheets and other maths games so that children can choose a maths task while you are busy with your focus group.

◆ Using the differentiated activity sheets

Activity 1 is for those children who are likely to struggle with the content of the lesson and who need a simple task, often with lower numbers than other groups. Activity 2 is for children who seem to have grasped the main ideas during the whole-class starter, and Activity 3 for those who need a more challenging task.

The book symbol at the bottom of some activity pages indicates further work to be done in maths books, or on the maths table, but unless you have a helper, this might be the time to suggest playing a maths game instead.

◆ Plenary session

This suggests ideas for a whole-class review to discuss the learning outcomes, and gives questions to ask so that children have a chance to reflect on what they have learned and for the teacher to assess their knowledge and understanding. This session is often about five or ten minutes long.

◆ Further activities

This is a list of further activities that can be developed from the lessons to give children more experience with the learning objectives.

◆ Extension

These are ideas for how to take children on and give them more difficult tasks.

◆ Support

These are ideas for children who are going to need more support before they have grasped the learning objectives.

◆ The use of calculators

Although children may not be using calculators very much at Key Stage 1, and they will certainly not use them for calculating, they can be very helpful in focusing children on number patterns, place value and so on. In Year 1, calculators are invaluable for teaching number recognition and an understanding of conventional symbols, such as the addition sign. We need to have them in the classroom, in the play shop and so on, so that the children are free to explore the wonder and excitement of number through using these powerful tools.

GENERIC SHEETS

On pages 90 to 94 there are some generic sheets that give extra help with key skills for Year 1 children. These sheets can be photocopied with different numbers on them to suit your different groups. Guidance on using them is given in the lesson plans or in the further activities.

ASSESSMENT

At the top of most of the activity sheets there is a row of three small boxes. These link with your assessment of how well the child has grasped the intended learning for that lesson. On page 5 there is a list of the assessment criteria for both lessons for each chapter (for the photocopiable activity sheets these are in italics) and you can use these criteria to decide how well a child has grasped the content of a particular lesson. They should be used as follows:

✦ If the child seems not to have grasped the concept, tick the first box.
✦ If there is evidence of the child having learned what you intended, tick the second box.
✦ Tick the third box for children who have a very secure grasp of the lesson and you think can use and apply the concept.

Of course, there will often not be evidence on the sheet that corresponds with your observations of some children's understandings, so you will need to make a note (on the sheet if you want) of what those children said or did to back up why you ticked a particular box. With young children, recording on sheets is often not going to assess understanding, especially where the lesson is about some acquisition of essential language. We need to listen to children very carefully. Assessment is much broader than children's recordings, so your additional annotations based on your observations are important.

At the end of each half term, flicking through each child's sheets can give you a basis for your teacher assessments, and will enable you to plan for your next half term.

In addition to this assessment on the children's sheets, there is a 'brick wall' on page 95 that outlines the basic concepts and skills for a secure understanding of counting. Generally, these are the lower bricks and some other aspects of early number understanding are on higher bricks. (It isn't possible to give an exact order of learning as it varies so much.)

It is absolutely crucial that we do counting every day to give children a firm foundation for later maths work. You can use this brick wall as a flexible resource and photocopy it for each child or group you are concerned about and who seems not to be counting securely yet.

There is space for you to add other learning objectives, or concepts that the child seems now to understand, or to note their targets for the next half term. As you observe children in mental maths time and playing on the maths table, note their progress and look at the gaps they have and set up relevant structured play. (The brick wall will also be relevant for use with other older children who still are not secure with counting.)

On page 96 there is a blank copy of the brick wall for you to photocopy and use for groups or individuals in any way you choose, maybe putting on the bricks the learning objectives just for one term for one group, so that you can keep a check on progress. The idea is that this should both support your target setting for groups and individuals and the way your school does assessments.

Year 1 Assessment Criteria

Chapter 1
+ *Can count to 20/name teen numbers/ understand if objects are rearranged, number stays the same.*
+ Can give simple estimates and check by counting.

Chapter 2
+ Can compare and order numbers to 20.
+ *Can add 1/10 more to numbers and say what is 1/10 less than numbers to 20 and above.*

Chapter 3
+ *Can count in 2s, 5s and 10s.*
+ Can predict other even numbers from a simple pattern.

Chapter 4
+ Can talk about 'is it true that you can add numbers in any order?'
+ *Can use a wide range of language for addition and relate to symbols + and =.*

Chapter 5
+ Can understand subtraction as taking away.
+ *Can understand counting back on a number line.*

Chapter 6
+ Can partition a teens number into tens and ones.
+ *Can identify near-doubles and use known doubles to calculate.*

Chapter 7
+ *Can see that putting the larger number first speeds up calculating.*
+ Can split into 5 and a bit to aid calculating and then recombine.

Chapter 8
+ Can choose and use appropriate operations and mental strategies to solve problems.

+ *Can solve mathematical puzzles with number/shape and explain methods and reasoning.*

Chapter 9
+ *Can recognise all coins and add up small amounts.*
+ *Can give change to 10/20p.*

Chapter 10
+ *Can talk about passage of time and read o'clock times.*
+ Can make up small amounts of money.

Chapter 11
+ *Can compare lengths and use appropriate standard and non-standard units.*
+ Can solve simple word problems involving length, mass and capacity and explain how problems were solved.

Chapter 12
+ Can sort objects into sets, create and interpret simple block graphs.
+ *Can sort using a simple tree diagram.*

Chapter 13
+ Can use 2D shapes to make patterns and solve problems/puzzles and explain reasoning.
+ *Can talk about properties of 3D shapes and make models.*

Chapter 14
+ Can follow instructions and understand language of position.
+ *Can use everyday language to describe direction/movement.*

The criteria in italics are those that relate to the children's activity sheets.

Counting and estimating

✦ Overall learning objectives

✦ Say the number names in order to 20 and back to zero.
✦ Count reliably to 20 objects and know that if the objects are rearranged the number stays the same.
✦ Count 'teen' numbers as a ten and some units.
✦ Give a sensible estimate and then check by counting.

✦ LESSON ONE HOW MANY?

✦ Assessment focus

Can the children count to 20 reliably, naming 'teen' numbers, and understand that if the objects are rearranged, the number stays the same?

✦ Resources

✦ cubes/teddies
✦ cards with small pictures, stickers or stamps for estimating

✦ Oral work and mental calculation

Counting to 20/100

✦ Count to 10 then 20 every day for several weeks. Count from zero to 20 and back again. Do it in different ways, whispering, shouting, using silly voices, or round the circle with the 10th/20th child clapping their hands or jumping up. Count in 2s, saying all the even numbers loudly and whispering the odd ones. Count in 5s and 10s. Count to 100 round the circle, with the children who say the multiples of 10 jumping up.

✦ Starting point: whole class

✦ Each child needs a large handful of cubes – a number above 10. Sit in the circle and ask them to count their cubes and arrange them in a 'ten train' and some more so that you can see at a glance if they have counted correctly. Ask them to compare the length of their ten train with the children next to them – they should be the same length. Ask everyone to put their cubes in a line. How many? Then ask them to put all their cubes in a little pile all together. Ask how many. Observe carefully who wants to count them again. These children need to do Activity sheet 1. Those who understand that the number remains the same however the cubes are arranged can do either Activity sheet 2 or 3. (Put sticky tape around your 'ten trains' and keep them in a box for counting and mental maths. You might like each train to be just one colour.)

✦ Group activities

Focus group

Use Activity sheet 1. The children count out a 'teen' number of objects and put them on the whale, writing the number in the space. Then they move them to the long sea snake. Ask them how many there are now. *"Do you really need to count them again?"* Establish that they didn't add any, or take any away, so there must still be the same number. Some children will need repeated practice with this.

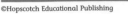

Counting and estimating

 Teacher-independent groups

Use the photocopiable activity sheets.

Activity sheet 1: As for the focus group.

Activity sheet 2: The children should complete the number line then count the fish and write the 'teen' numbers. These are in order to 15.

Activity sheet 3: These children should first complete the number line which goes to 21. They then need to add together the fish in the nets with those swimming free. In the last part they should draw 10 fish in the net and another 10 (which they might decide should also be in a net). They should

then consider how they would show 21 fish (two nets and a single fish?)

✦ *Plenary session*

✦ Go over the rearrangement of cubes and explain how there is no need to count. Note who needs more help with this.

✦ Choose 11 children from groups 2 and 3 to hold up cards 10 to 20 and put themselves in order. In pairs, the children should show 'teen' numbers with their fingers, so one child holds up the ten and the other the ones. Ask children from group 1 to come and count the fingers. Demonstrate how there is no need to count the 10 fingers each time. *"We know there are 10."*

LESSON TWO
ESTIMATE AND COUNT

✦ *Assessment focus*

Can the children give a sensible estimate and then check by counting?

✦ *Resources*

✦ picture cards
✦ cubes
✦ number cards
✦ see-through containers

✦ *Oral work and mental calculation*

Linking addition and subtraction

✦ Give each child a 'ten train' and demonstrate ways to split 10 by hiding all the cubes behind your back and bringing out just 2 of them. Ask how many are still behind your back. Repeat this several times with different numbers. Go around the circle with each child hiding some behind their back and asking the others a question, for

example *"I've got 10 cubes altogether and you can see 4. How many are hiding?"*

✦ Give the children experience with empty-box problems, such as ☐ + 2 =10, (*"something add 2 makes 10"*), asking them to find the 'something'. Write the other number sentences you can make with 2, 8 and 10, for example 2 + 8 = 10, 10 – 2 = 8 and 10 – 8 = 2.

✦ *Starting point: whole class*

✦ Make cards with 9, 11, 19 and 21 pictures on them (use stamper pens). Ask, *"Is this number nearer 5 or nearer 10?"* (It seems to help children to make estimates if we suggest some numbers. It can help to suggest numbers that are completely over the top, so showing a card with 19 pictures, you can ask *"Is this nearer 20 or nearer 100?"*)

✦ Let the children make estimates of things that can be counted but not touched. *"Do you think we have about 14 window panes in our class or about 100?"*

✦ Use familiar numbers. *"We have 32 children in our class. Guess how many children are in class 3."*

✦ In a circle, some children take a handful of cubes, then everyone estimates how many they have taken. Then count them.

Counting and estimating

◆ Group activities

Focus group

Make estimates using cards or collections of objects, then count them. Put sweets or cubes in a see-through jar, first estimating, then counting in groups of ten. Make sure the children understand that an estimate is a guess and that it doesn't matter if they don't get their estimate right. You don't expect estimates to be exactly right.

Teacher-independent groups

Group 1: Give out the number cards 9, 10 and 11 (some might manage 19, 20 and 21) and ask the children to count out the right number of objects on to a board or tray for the plenary session.

Group 2: With the children working in pairs, they take two handfuls of cubes, write down a guess of how many, then count them, grouping them in tens. Bring one attempt to review time.

Group 3: These children should put objects into see-through containers, such as plastic jugs, make guesses at how many then secretly count them carefully and record the number.

◆ Plenary session

◆ Ask the group 1 children to count their objects so that you can check their counting. *"So you have some numbers that are round about 10. 9 and 11 are almost 10."* Ask them to select from your estimation cards used in the starter session those cards that are 'almost 10'.

◆ Look at the estimates made by group 2 and find numbers on the 100 square or number line. *"You made an estimate of 17 and there were 21. You were very close. Let's count up on our fingers from 17 to 21 and find the difference."*

◆ Ask the children to make guesses of how many in the group-3 and focus-group containers. Find the numbers on the 100 square.

◆ *"What did you enjoy doing in maths today?"*

◆ *"When you have made a guess or estimate of how many, how can you find out exactly how many?"* (Count.)

◆ Further activities

◆ Teach the children to play a simple counting game using generic sheet 1 (page 90). Players take turns to throw the dice and move that many spaces along the track with a counter. First to get to the undersea treasure wins a gold coin. Let children play the game often and keep a tally on the wall of how many gold coins each child has won, and use it for counting, estimating and mental maths.

◆ Estimate in many different contexts, guessing measures and numbers, for example *"How many strides across our carpet?"* or *"How many children on that PE mat?"*

◆ Extension

◆ *"About how many children do you think there are in the school/dots on this bit of paper? Make a guess then try to find out."*

◆ Support

◆ Count between 5 and 20 objects/fingers every day and keep singing number rhymes.

◆ Set group targets for counting and involve parents to support the counting.

✦ How many cubes? ✦

✦ Put your cubes on the whale.

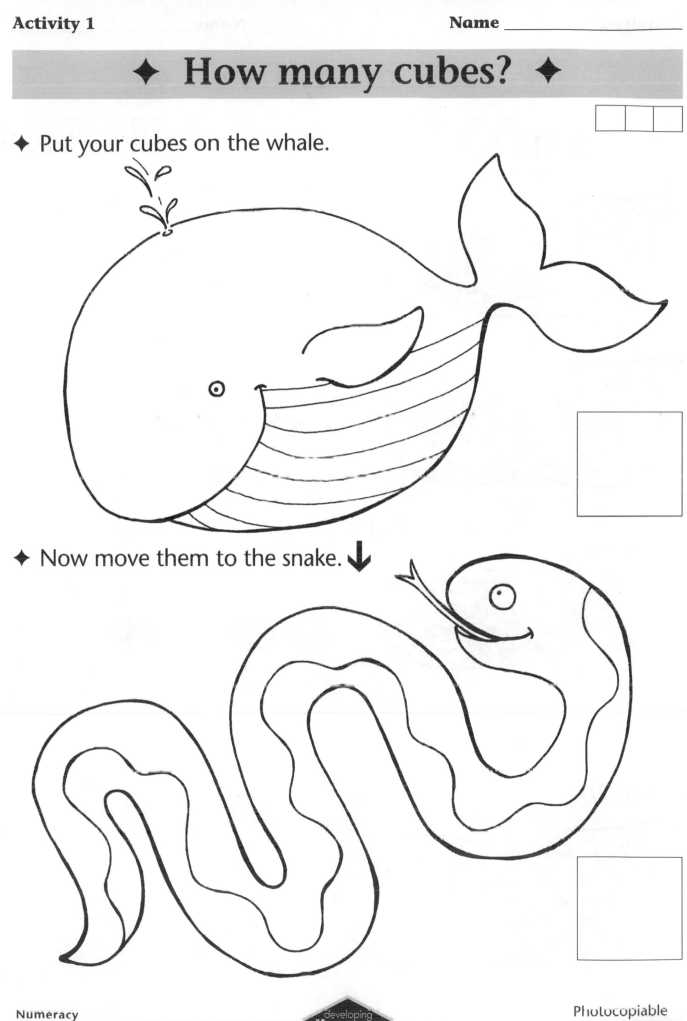

✦ Now move them to the snake. ↓

✦ How many fish? ✦

9	10	11			14	15			19

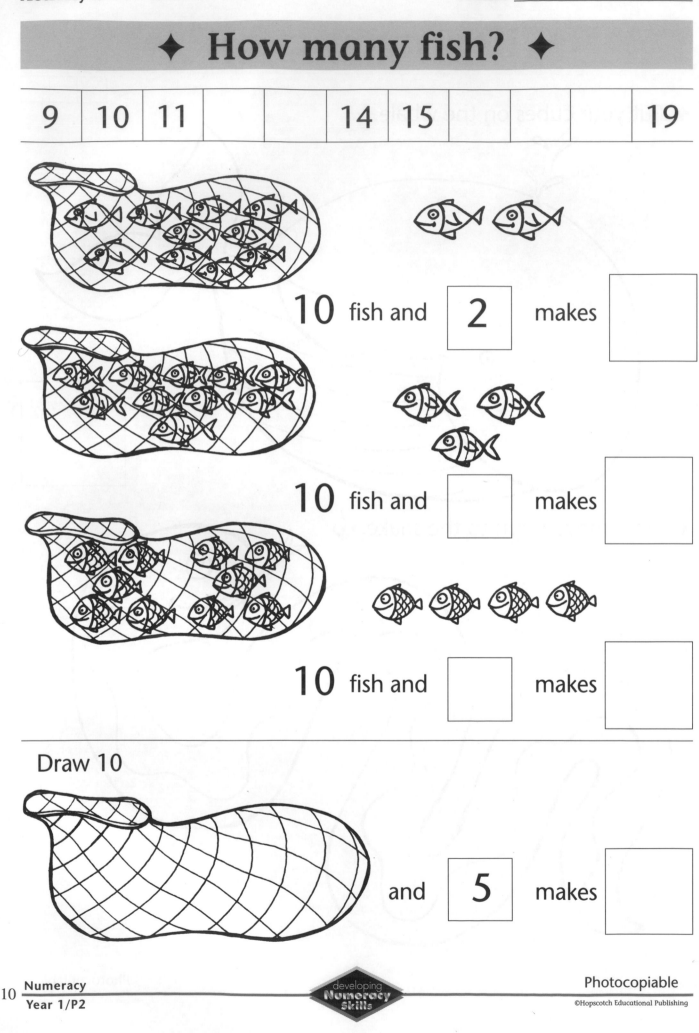

10 fish and [2] makes [ ]

10 fish and [ ] makes [ ]

10 fish and [ ] makes [ ]

Draw 10

and [5] makes [ ]

developing
Numeracy Skills

Photocopiable
©Hopscotch Educational Publishing

✦ How many fish? ✦

11		13			16	17				21

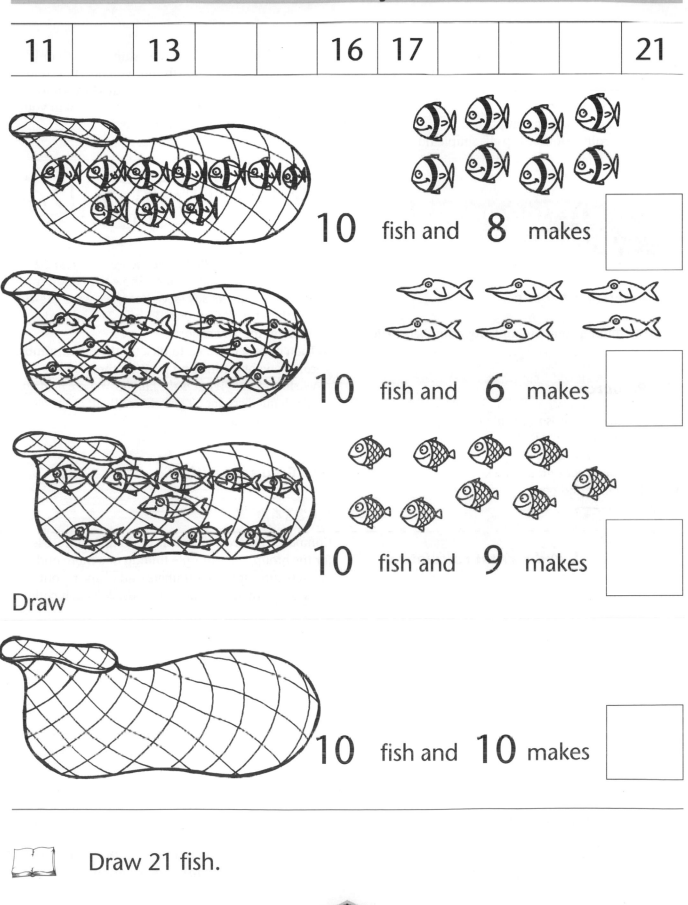

10 fish and 8 makes ☐

10 fish and 6 makes ☐

10 fish and 9 makes ☐

Draw

10 fish and 10 makes ☐

Draw 21 fish.

11

Ordering numbers

◆ Overall learning objectives

◆ Count on and back in ones and tens from small numbers, including zero.
◆ Understand zero as the empty set.
◆ Explain orally relationships in simple number sentences, such as ☐ + 10 = 12.

LESSON ONE
COMPARE AND ORDER

◆ Assessment focus

Can the children compare and order numbers to 20?

◆ Resources

◆ 'teen' number cards in numbers and words
◆ sets of number cards 0–20
◆ rods, cubes, yoghurt pots
◆ squares of paper and Blu-tack
◆ washing line and pegs
◆ 100 squares

◆ Oral work and mental calculation

Tens and units

◆ Play 'What's my number?' Demonstrate a number shown with your fingers – 31 would be shown by holding up 10 fingers 3 times then 1. (You need to make children wait until they are sure all the number has been shown before they call out.) When children are confident, take turns around the circle to show a number. (Let children pass if they want to.) Link numbers to an abacus and 100 square.

◆ Starting point: whole class

◆ Put number cards 0–20 in the middle of the circle and ask five children to pick one up. Order this

selection of numbers on a washing line. Count fingers in pairs. Establish that you don't need to keep counting the 10 fingers because we know there are 10. Demonstrate holding the 10 in your head and counting on with fingers.

◆ *"Tell me a number that comes between 14 and 20. Write that number in the air."* Show the children how although we say 'seventeen' we write the 10 first then the 7. Compare 17 and 71 and find them on the 100 square.
◆ Then choose children to pick up the other number cards one at a time and position them on the washing line. *"What is the number you are holding? Which numbers does it go next to? What is one more than your number?"*

◆ Group activities

 Focus group

Compare and order numbers at an appropriate level for the group, for example finding one more and one less than specific numbers and counting out objects to match the number cards. Ask each child individually to order the number cards from 0 to 20 and ask questions such as *"Tell me a number that is 2 more than 17."*

 Teacher-independent groups

Group 1: Provide number cards or yoghurt pots numbered 0–20 and ask this group to put them in order and write the numbers in their books. (They could copy the numbers on to a prepared strip of paper for Lesson Two, Activities 1 and 2, when they will need a number line.) They can count out some of the teen numbers with ten rods and units or Unifix 'ten trains' and put them in the yoghurt pots ready for checking at the plenary session.

developing
Numeracy
Skills

Ordering numbers

Group 2: Make a 'staircase' of rods or Unifix from 10 to 20 in order, all of the tens in one colour and the units in another colour. The children could match their rods to cards with teen numbers written in words. If there is time they could use small paper bags and pretend sweets to make bags of 10 for use at mental maths time.

Group 3: Provide squares of paper (about 10cm by 10cm) and Blu-tack and ask children to start to build up a 100 square on a board. They can write one number on each bit of paper in pencil first and go over them (after they have been checked) with pen.

✦ Plenary session

✦ Go over the work from each group. Remind the children how to write a 'teen' number with the 1 for the 10 first.

✦ Order a set of cards from 0 to 20 on the washing line. The children shut their eyes and you swap two cards. *"Which cards did I move? How do you know that?"* Demonstrate how the tens number stays the same – it is a 1 – from 10 all the way to 19, but the units numbers change. (There is more work on this in Chapter 6, Lesson One.)

✦ *"Today we learned about ordering numbers and writing 'teen' numbers. Tell me something you learned today."*

✦ Count the sweets in bags of 10 (10, 20, and so on).

LESSON TWO
MORE AND LESS

✦ Assessment focus

Can the children add 1 more and 10 more to numbers and say what is 1 less and 10 less than numbers to 20 and above?

✦ Resources

✦ 100 square
✦ number cards in numbers and words

✦ Oral work and mental calculation

Mixed number work

✦ Use the paper 100 square made by group 3 in Lesson One. Ask some children to come and point to numbers. Say *"How do you write 15? How is it different from 51? Let's take off all the even numbers in the first two rows"* (2, 4, 6, 8, etc). *"Now let's say the odd numbers."* In pairs, make 16 with your fingers, one person with 10 fingers, the other with the units. *"Come and point to a 2-digit number that has 3 tens and some units."*

✦ Starting point: whole class

✦ Tell the children that they are going to find out about adding and taking away 1. Hold up some number cards and ask *"What is 1 more than this number?"* Work it out using fingers and show the step of 1 on the number line and 100 square. Move on to 1 less than a number. Use the cards again and ask for 10 more and 10 less. (See also Chapter 6, Lesson One.) Again, work it out with fingers in pairs and repeat until the children can respond quickly. Ask them to tell you about the pattern made when adding 10 to a single-digit number. (The unit stays the same number and there is a 1 for the 10 in front of it.)

✦ Make number sentences with cards with words and number symbols, such as '1 more than 4 is …' and relate this to $1 + 4 = \boxed{}$. Make it clear that finding 1 more is adding 1 and 1 less is the same as taking away or counting back 1. Keep the number sentences on display as the children do their activity sheets to help them to find missing bits of equations (empty-box problems). If you display $3 + 10 = 13$, you can take away the 3 so you have $\boxed{} + 10 = 13$. (See the oral work in Chapter 1, Lesson Two.) Ask questions such as *"What do I need to add to 10 to make 13?"* and

developing
**Numeracy
Skills**

Ordering numbers

"I've got a number in my head. When I add 10 to it, I get 16. What is the number in my head?" (It is very important that children experience number sentences in a variety of forms.)

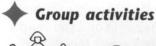

◆ Group activities

Focus group

Give these children more experience with empty-box problems, making the calculations with cards and Blu-tack ready to take to the plenary session. For example, *"Something and 1 more makes 6."* If they are confused, repeat the oral maths from Chapter 1, Lesson Two, hiding objects behind your back.

Teacher-independent groups

Use the photocopiable activity sheets.

Activity sheet 1: Point out the sections that are '1 more' and '1 less'. The children can use the number lines they made in Lesson One to show hopping on along the number line with their fingers.

Activity sheet 2: Point out the sections that are 'more' and those where they need to find 10 less. Provide number lines/tracks.

Activity sheet 3: Encourage these children to choose numbers beyond 20 if they want. Provide a 100 square. (Generic sheet 5 on page 94.)

◆ Plenary session

✦ Ask group 1 to tell you some of their '1 more' and '1 less', making sure they are relating these to the + and – signs. Ask them oral questions about 10 more and 10 less.

✦ Groups 2 and 3 children can demonstrate their 'more' and 'less' on a 100 square and make number sentences with cards and Blu-tack and read them out. For example *"Something add 10 makes 17. The 'something' is 7."*

✦ *"Today you were learning about 1 more and 10 more, and 1 less and 10 less. Someone tell me something they have learned today."*

◆ Further activities

✦ Keep a washing line up and order numbers every day for a few weeks.

◆ Extension

✦ Some children might be ready to think about 100 more, or even 1000 more. If you don't already have a number line up to and then beyond 100, let children make one. (Generic sheets 3 and 4, pages 92–93.)

◆ Support

✦ Link '1 more' to steps on the floor number line.

✦ At mental maths time, target specific children with '1 more than' and '1 less than' questions until they are confident. Then move on to 10 more and less using a 100 square.

◆ More than and less than ◆

1 more than 2 is 3

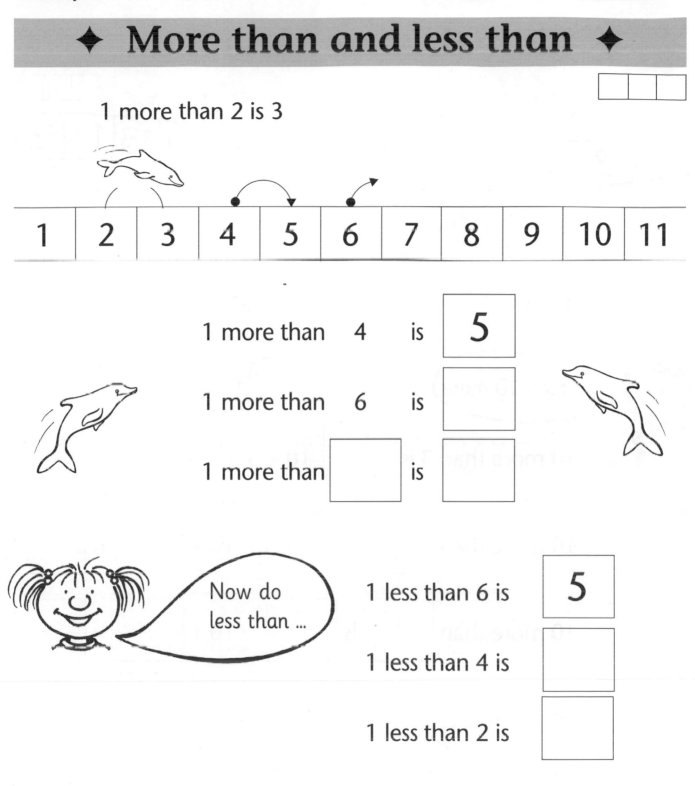

1 more than   4   is | 5 |

1 more than   6   is | |

1 more than | | is | |

Now do less than ...

1 less than 6 is | 5 |

1 less than 4 is | |

1 less than 2 is | |

Do take aways.   6 − 1 =
                      5 − 1 =

Photocopiable
©Hopscotch Educational Publishing

15

✦ More than and less than ✦

2 3 4 5 6 7 8 9 10 11 12 13 14 15

1 more than 3 is 4   1 + 3 = ☐

1 more than 5 is ☐   1 + 5 = ☐

Find 10 more

10 more than 3 is ☐   10 + 3 = ☐

10 more than ☐ is ☐   10 + ☐ = ☐

10 more than ☐ is ☐   10 + ☐ = ☐

Find 10 less

10 less than   13   is ☐

10 less than ☐   is ☐

Do some take-away 10s.   13 – 10 =   15 – 10 =

developing **Numeracy Skills**

Photocopiable
©Hopscotch Educational Publishing

Counting in 2s, 5s and 10s

◆ Overall learning objectives

◆ Explain methods and reasoning orally.
◆ Count in 2s, 5s and 10s (later, 3s and 4s).
◆ Investigate the statement 'all even numbers end in zero, 2, 4, 6 or 8'.
◆ Predict from a simple pattern.

◆ LESSON ONE
COUNT AND MATCH

◆ Assessment focus

Can the children count in 2s, 5s and 10s?

◆ Resources

◆ about 60 play-dough 'buns' (or cubes)
◆ paper plates
◆ large 100 square and coloured pens
◆ pairs of shoes or socks
◆ paper starfish with five arms each

◆ Oral work and mental calculation

Counting in 10s and 5s

◆ The children chant "10, 20, 30" up to 100 all together, then, when they are confident, go around the circle. (They can just say 'pass' if they don't want a go.) When most are secure with this, the first child in the circle chooses a single-digit number, say 3, and then everyone chants "13, 23, 33, 43" and so on together. Again, when they are confident, you can do this around the circle.

◆ Play 'finger fives'. You show, say, three lots of five fingers, using just one hand, holding up the fingers clearly each time. The children count silently in their head, 5, 10, 15. You ask how many (15) and how many lots of 5 (3). Let them take turns to do a finger-fives number. Others can respond by holding up their own digit cards 0–9.

Ask "What do all the numbers end in when we play 'finger fives'?" (5 or 0.) If you can play where noise doesn't matter, the person showing the finger fives claps when they get to the end and the others try to shout out the number first.

◆ Starting point: whole class

◆ Teach the children to chant numbers counting in 10s (to 100), 5s and 2s to 20 then 30. (You can do each number separately in three different lessons.) Count 10 fingers, 5 arms on each starfish and shoes in pairs. Show these numbers on a 100 square and let the children explain the patterns. "The numbers when you count in 5s end in 5 or zero."

◆ Put the children in groups of 3, 4 or 5 and give them a number that they must make with their fingers. For example, a group of 5 children makes 25 with each child holding up 5 fingers. The group then count in 5s up to 25. Ask "What is 5 less than/more than 25? How many children had to hold up 5 fingers to make 25? So 5 lots of 5 makes 25. How many is 4 groups of 5?" Relate fingers to starfish arms.

◆ Count pairs of shoes or socks in 2s. Draw a number line to 10 as on Activity sheet 1 and ask a child to circle and name the even numbers counting in 2s from zero (2, 4, 6 and so on). Leave this up on display.

◆ Group activities

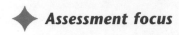   Focus group

Arrange objects into groups of 2, or 5 or 10. The children find the related number cards.

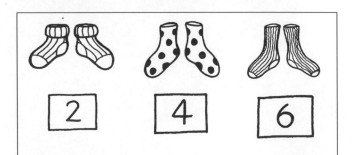

18
©Hopscotch Educational Publishing

developing
Numeracy
Skills

Numeracy
Year 1/P2

Counting in 2s, 5s and 10s

Teacher-independent groups

Use the photocopiable activity sheets.

Activity sheet 1: This is just counting in 2s. Give the children socks or shoes to work with.

Activity sheet 2: Provide socks and paper starfish to help the children do this activity sheet.

Activity sheet 3: These children count in 2s and 5s. Provide a 100 square.

◆ Plenary session

- ◆ *"Let's all count in 2s. Count our pairs of shoes. How many shoes? How many lots of 2?"*
- ◆ *"Let's see how far we can count in 2s/5s."*
- ◆ Help children who have counted up to and beyond 100 to write numbers such as 102.

◆ LESSON TWO ◆ ESTIMATE AND COUNT

◆ Assessment focus

Can the children predict other even numbers from a simple pattern?

◆ Oral work and mental calculation

Adding three numbers

- ◆ Divide the children into the fishes and the whales. The fishes win a point if the number is 10 or below. The whales win a point if the number is above 10. They take turns to throw three dice and add the numbers mentally. (If they are sitting at tables it can be quicker for you to throw the dice in front of each child in turn.) Demonstrate how 1 + 2 + 6 can be added more quickly if we start with holding the 6 in our head and counting on the smaller numbers with fingers.

◆ Starting point: whole class

- ◆ Explain that the lesson today is about some very special numbers called even numbers. Using a large 100 square show the children how to count

in 2s along the top line, missing out every other number. They could do this by saying all the numbers, but saying the odd ones very quietly and the even ones very loudly. Colour the even numbers in some way. Demonstrate the even numbers to 10 with fingers, showing how you can make those numbers with the same number of fingers on each hand. Demonstrate with play-dough buns that an even number shares out evenly between two people.

- ◆ *"Now let's look at the second row of the 100 square. Can you tell me how to go on with our pattern of counting in 2s?"* Continue colouring the pattern so that vertical lines are appearing on the 100 square. Share out play-dough buns again to check that the numbers are even. Ask for predictions for even numbers in the next row. Ask them to look carefully at the endings of even numbers. (They all end in either 0, 2, 4, 6 or 8.) *"So do you think 29 is an even number?"*

◆ Group activities

Focus group

- ◆ Use a 100 square to continue the pattern to see if children can predict even numbers on the next line. Ask them to explain their reasoning. (With those who still need lots of support, assess the progress of each individual child with counting and one-to-one correspondence. *"Count out 20 cubes"* – check to see how accurate they are.)

◆ How many boots? ◆

◆ **Colour the even numbers.**

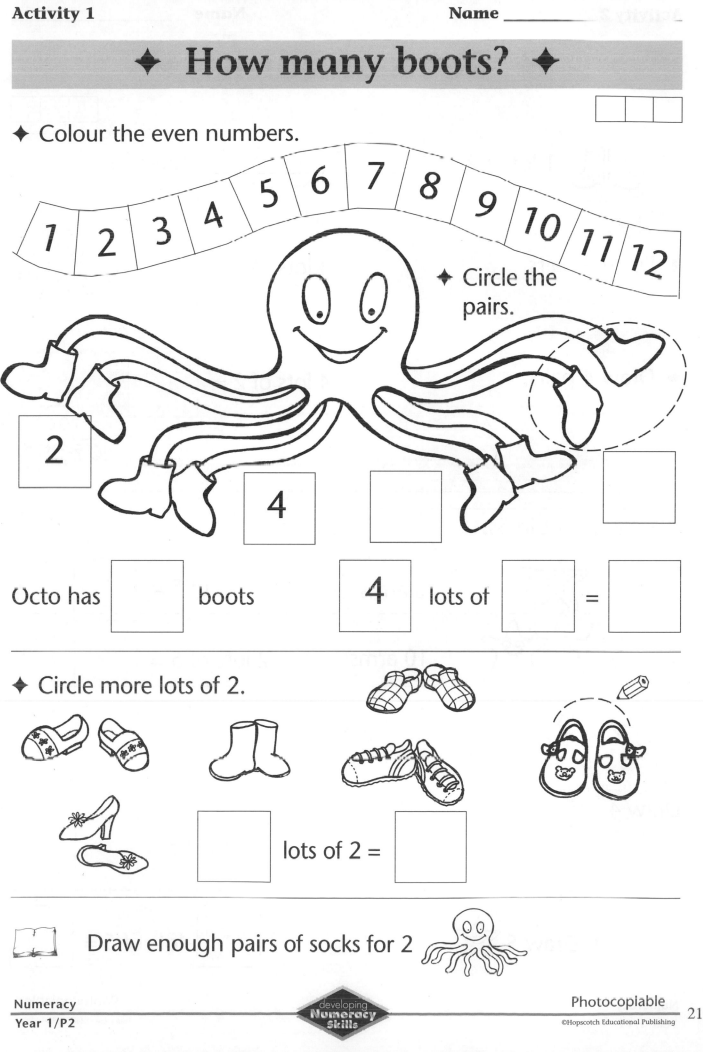

1 2 3 4 5 6 7 8 9 10 11 12

◆ Circle the
pairs.

2   4

Octo has [ ] boots   4 lots of [ ] = [ ]

◆ Circle more lots of 2.

[ ] lots of 2 = [ ]

Draw enough pairs of socks for 2

21

Name _____

✦ Boots and arms ✦

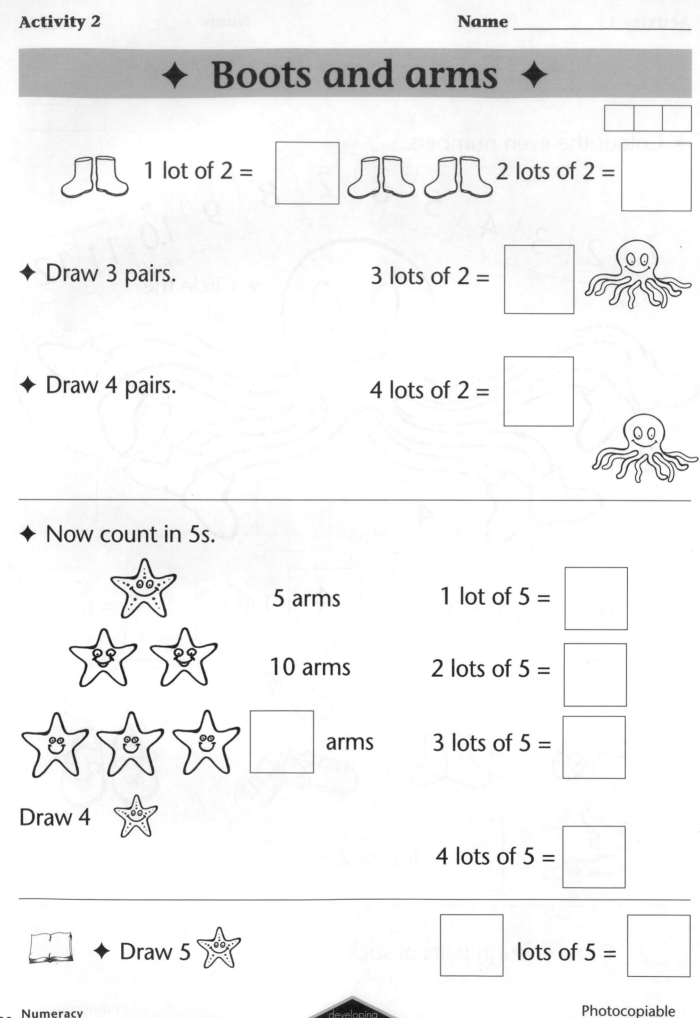

1 lot of 2 =

2 lots of 2 =

✦ Draw 3 pairs.

3 lots of 2 =

✦ Draw 4 pairs.

4 lots of 2 =

✦ Now count in 5s.

5 arms

1 lot of 5 =

10 arms

2 lots of 5 =

_____ arms

3 lots of 5 =

Draw 4

4 lots of 5 =

✦ Draw 5

_____ lots of 5 =

✦ 2s and 5s ✦

✦ Colour the even numbers.

1	2	3	4	5	6	7	8	9	10
11	12	13	14	15	16	17	18	19	20
21	22	23	24	25	26	27	28	29	30
31	32	33	34	35	36	37	38	39	40
41	42	43	44	45	46	47	48	49	50

I can count in 2s up to _____

✦ Now count in 5s.

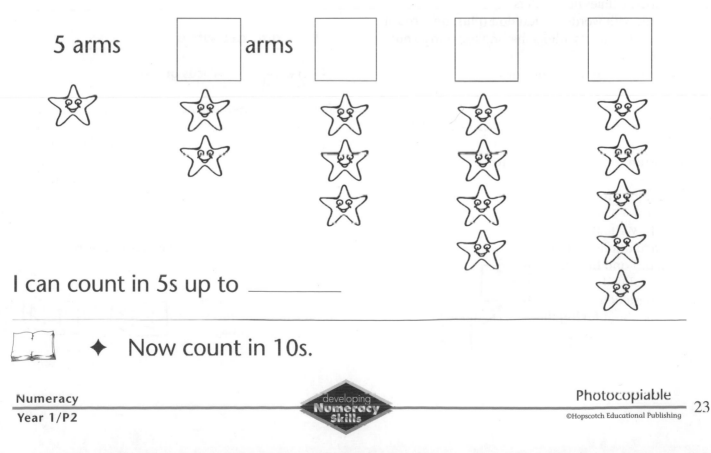

5 arms　　▢　arms　　▢　　　　▢　　　　▢

I can count in 5s up to _____

✦ Now count in 10s.

Addition

✦ Overall learning objectives

✦ Understand the operation of addition and the related vocabulary.

✦ Begin to recognise that addition can be done in any order and investigate the general statement 'you can add numbers in any order'.

✦ Understand that more than two numbers can be added.

✦ Know by heart addition facts up to 5/10.

LESSON ONE
CHANGE IT AROUND

✦ Assessment focus

Can the children talk about the question: *"Is it true that you can add numbers in any order?"*

✦ Resources

✦ large and small number lines 0–20

✦ Unifix cubes with numbers written on the four faces to make dice

✦ cubes, teddies or counters

✦ cards with words for addition (plus, and, count on, add, equals, altogether makes, and so on)

✦ Blu-tack

✦ number and operation cards

✦ Oral work and mental calculation

Addition and subtraction with 4

✦ Ask for ways of making 4 (1 + 3 = 4, 4 + 0 = 4, 2 + 2 = 4). Write the calculations on the board and then find the related subtractions.

✦ Talk about taking the 1 away again and getting back to 3.

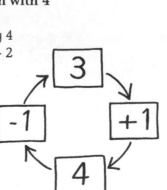

✦ Make sure the children can see that a subtraction undoes an addition. Give repeated practice with number bonds to 4, then on another day move on to 5, then 10, then 20.

✦ Starting point: whole class

✦ Tell the children that the lesson today is about adding numbers in a different order. Ask two children to come to the front to play 'finger wizz'. They hide their hands behind their back and on the count of 1, 2, 3 they bring out one hand with some fingers up and others down. Count the fingers with the children. *"Tom has 4 fingers and Jacob has 2. Hold the 4 in your head and count on the 2, … 5, 6. So that is 6 fingers altogether. Now let's do it the other way. This time hold the 2 in our head and count on the 4 … 3, 4, 5, 6. We get to 6 again."* (This is revisited in Chapter 7.)

✦ *"So do you think you can add numbers in any order?"* Repeat this several times, bringing out a different number of fingers. Write the calculations on the board and show them on a number line.

✦ Move on to larger numbers using two hands each. Establish that whatever order you do it in, the answer is the same.

✦ Group activities

 Focus group

Repeat the starter, asking the children to make the number sentence with cards and to choose the right operation card. Another child reverses the sentence, doing the addition in a different order. Give extra practice with mental recall of number bonds to 4 and 5 for those who need it.

 Teacher-independent groups

Group 1: Write the numbers 1, 2, 3 and 4 on the four side faces of two Unifix cubes.

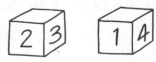

Addition

Throw the cubes and write the two numbers they land on (throw again if one lands on the top or bottom). Get out that many plastic teddies or cubes and add them. Record your answer. Suggest to the children that they draw the teddies or cubes and find the right number card for the answer.

Group 2: Use three Unifix cubes with numbers written on them to suit this group. Throw the cubes and write down the numbers they land on. Add them up, then write them in a different order and add them again.

Group 3: Use three or four Unifix cubes numbered to suit this group. They throw the cubes and add the numbers they land on, then add them again in a different order.

✦ *Plenary session*

- ✦ Group 1: *"What would happen if you did 1 + 3 as 3 +1? Let's do it on your fingers."*
- ✦ *"Tell us what happens when you add up three numbers in a different order."* (You still get the same answer.)
- ✦ *"So do you think it is true to say that you can add numbers in any order and you still get the same answer?"*
- ✦ *"What have you learned today about adding?"*
- ✦ (If you are moving on to subtraction soon, ask if they think you can do subtraction in any order and get the same answer. No.)

✦ ✦ ✦ ✦ ✦ ✦ ✦ ✦ ✦ ✦ ✦ ✦

✦ LESSON TWO WORDS AND SYMBOLS

✦ *Assessment focus*

Can the children use a wide range of language for addition and relate words to the symbols + and =?

✦ *Oral work and mental calculation*

The language of addition and adding two/three numbers

- ✦ Ask the children to hold up fingers for the numbers you give them, such as *"2 and another 2 and 3"*. Use a wide range of language. *"5 plus 1 and another 1. 4 add on 2 more and another 3. 6 plus 1 plus another 2 altogether makes … ? 4 add 2 plus 2 equals … ?"* They can come and write the calculations on the board.

✦ *Starting point: whole class*

- ✦ Use a large floor or wall number line and, using a wide range of vocabulary, demonstrate steps along it. (When you repeat this lesson, also show how counting back again means you get back to where you started, so 4 count on 3 lands on 7, count back the 3 and you get back to 4.)
- ✦ *"Ella, stand on (or point to) 2. Count on 3 steps. 1, 2, 3. Where do you think she will land? 2 count on 3, she lands on 5."* (Make sure all the children actually take one step and don't count as one the step they are on.)
- ✦ *"If Sam starts at 5 and takes 2 steps, where will he land? Make that into a number sentence. 5 and 2 more equals 7 altogether. Let's Blu-tack that sentence on to the board."* Make sure you use the words *'count on'* to prepare children for the activity sheets and relate counting on to other words for addition.
- ✦ In preparation for the group work, give pairs small number lines to practise taking steps along the line with their fingers. Check that they can link + to 'count on'. Demonstrate a number sentence with a + and = sign and do some 'empty-box' problems, such as ☐ – 3 = 4 (see Chapter 1, Lesson Two).

Addition

◆ Group activities

Focus group

Use this time to give more help with mental recall of number bonds or make more Blu-tacked number sentences to take to the plenary session, for example '3 and 4 more equals 7', with a related picture of that calculation on a number line.

Teacher-independent groups

Use the photocopiable activity sheets.

Activity sheet 1 Spend two minutes with this group at the start to check that they all take one step to get started and don't count the number they are on as 1! Children draw on their steps along the line.

Activity sheet 2: These children draw their steps along the line. They need to recognise + and =.

Activity sheet 3: Challenge these children to choose larger numbers. They can use a number line to 100 (see generic sheets 3 and 4 on pages 92 and 93).

All these groups can do further work on counting on using generic sheet 5 (page 94).

◆ Plenary session

◆ Let the children demonstrate their steps along their number lines on their activity sheets. Relate 'count on' to sentences with + and =.
◆ *"When we use the add symbol (+) what other words can we use?"* (Plus, count on, and.)

◆ Further activities

◆ Use dice, spinners and number wheels to give plenty of practice with adding. The number wheel below is made with two circles of card and a split pin and can be used for addition and subtraction.

◆ Extension

◆ Children can use generic sheets 3 and 4 (pages 92 and 93) to make long number lines up to 100 and make up some additions.
◆ Give children a handful of pennies to count.

◆ Support

◆ Use generic sheets 2 and 3 (pages 91 and 92) and a dice to practise counting on.
◆ Make small number cards 0–10 for number

bonds to 10 so that the number that makes up to 10 is on the back, for example 2 has 8 on the back, 9 has 1 on the back, and so on. The children play in pairs, asking each other what is the number on the back, then they check.

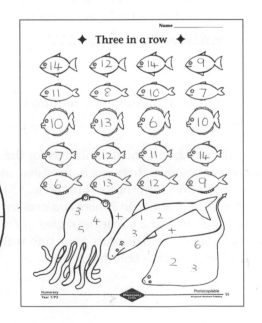

◆ Counting on ◆

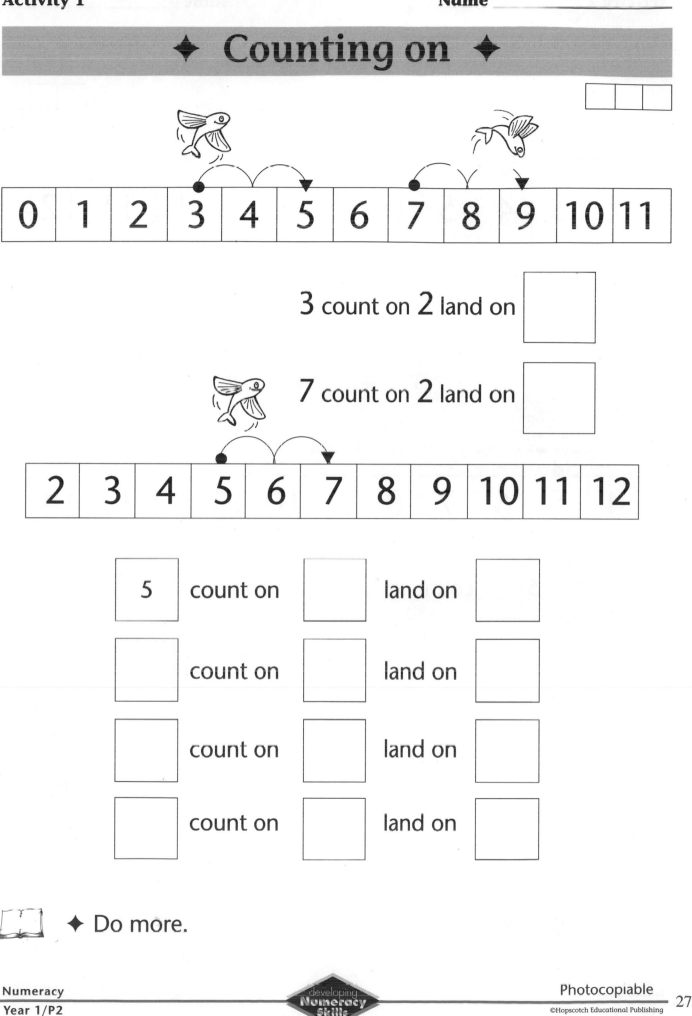

3 count on 2 land on

7 count on 2 land on

5   count on   land on

    count on   land on

    count on   land on

    count on   land on

◆ Do more.

✦ Counting on ✦

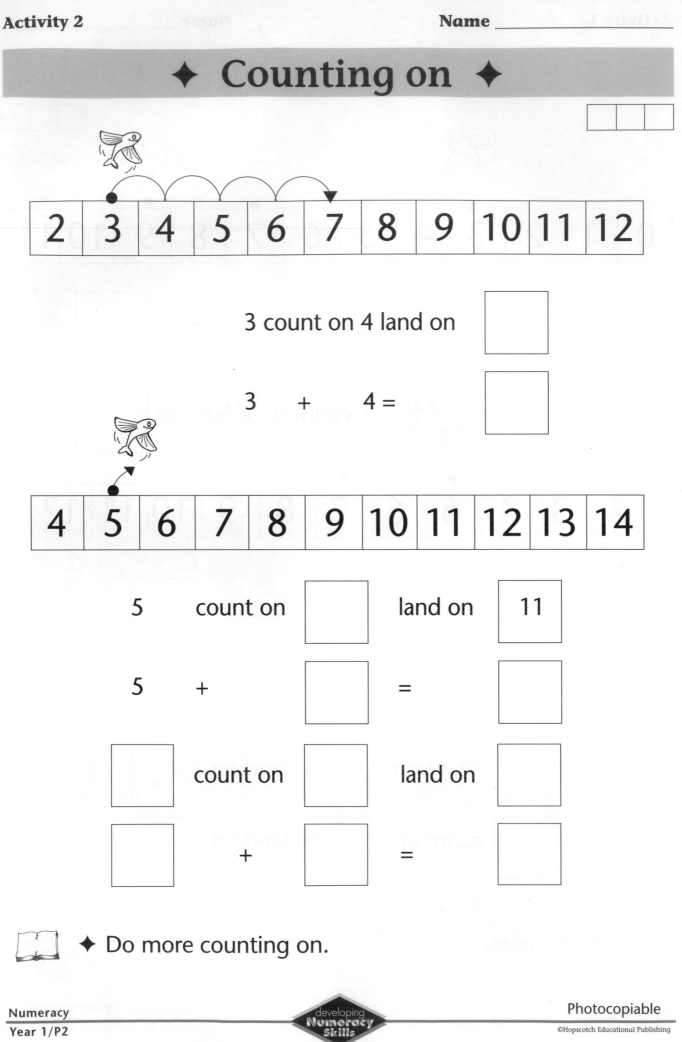

2	3	4	5	6	7	8	9	10	11	12

3 count on 4 land on ☐

3   +   4 = ☐

4	5	6	7	8	9	10	11	12	13	14

5   count on ☐   land on   11

5   +   ☐   =   ☐

☐   count on   ☐   land on   ☐

☐   +   ☐   =   ☐

📖 ✦ Do more counting on.

developing **Numeracy Skills**

Photocopiable
©Hopscotch Educational Publishing

✦ Counting on ✦

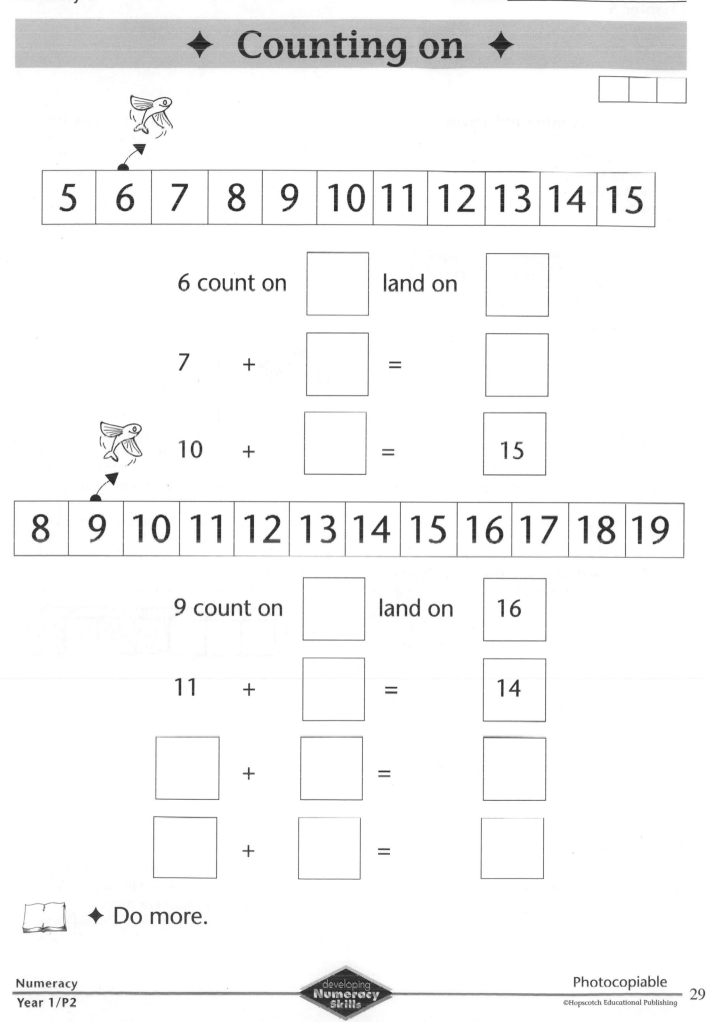

| 5 | 6 | 7 | 8 | 9 | 10 | 11 | 12 | 13 | 14 | 15 |

6 count on ☐ land on ☐

7   +   ☐   =   ☐

10   +   ☐   =   15

| 8 | 9 | 10 | 11 | 12 | 13 | 14 | 15 | 16 | 17 | 18 | 19 |

9 count on ☐ land on 16

11   +   ☐   =   14

☐   +   ☐   =   ☐

☐   +   ☐   =   ☐

✦ Do more.

29

Subtraction

✦ *Overall learning objectives*

✦ Understand subtraction as 'taking away', 'difference between', 'count back' and 'how many more to make' and the related vocabulary.

✦ Know by heart subtraction facts to 5/10.

LESSON ONE
TAKING AWAY

✦ *Assessment focus*

Can the children understand subtraction as taking away?

✦ *Resources*

✦ cards with vocabulary for subtraction ('take away', 'count back' and the – sign)

✦ Blu-tack

✦ cubes/teddies/counters

✦ *Oral work and mental calculation*

Mental subtractions

✦ Give practice with a wide range of language for subtraction. *"If I start with 3 apples and eat 1, how many are left?"*
"How many more do I need to add to 3 to make 5?"
"What number is 2 less than 6?"
"Hold up 10 fingers. Now fold down 3. How many left standing?"
"Surinder had 8 sweets and she ate half of them. How many left?"
"Shut your eyes and imagine you are standing on the number line on 7 and you count back 4 steps. Where will you end up?"

✦ *Starting point: whole class*

✦ Sit everyone in a circle, put five cubes in the middle and cover them with a cloth. Take out

three and show them. Ask how many are left under the cloth. (You can make up a story, such as *"5 frogs/dolphins in pool and 3 jump into another pool"*.) Check to see if they are right. Repeat this with different numbers. Sometimes hide the ones you take out, let them see how many are left under the cloth and ask them to work out how many you took away. Relate what you are doing to number sentences written on the board or on cards Blu-tacked to the wall.

✦ *Group activities*

 Focus group

✦ Use the vocabulary cards to make number sentences just with three numbers. For example, using 3, 4 and 7. '7 take away 4 is 3.' '4 less than 7 is 3.' 'The difference between 4 and 7 is 3.' '4 is 3 less than 7.' 'You need to add 3 to 4 to make it up to 7.' Blu-tack the sentences to the board for the plenary session. If these can be left for a few days they can be used as a basis for mental maths.

✦ Demonstrate 'difference between' using cube trains.

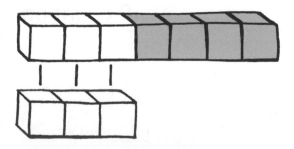

Teacher-independent groups

Group 1: Play the starter game in pairs with a cloth and about five teddies or other objects (to suit your children). Ask them to draw one number sentence such as 'five teddies and a big hand taking away two of them'.

Subtraction

Group 2: This group plays the starter game using ten cubes. One child hides the cubes behind a large book and shows how many are taken away. Let them have three goes each using different numbers, then they should draw pictures of three of those number sentences.

Group 3: This group also plays the starter game, using 12/15/20 cubes and cards and Blu-tack to make some number sentences to take to the plenary session, including the – sign.

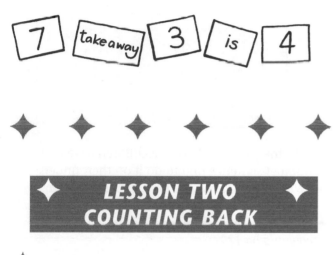

✦ Plenary session

✦ *"Harry started with 5 teddies and on his drawing you can see he took away 2 of them. How many did you have left? Tell me how to write that number sentence."*

✦ *"Sadia says that 10 take away 3 leaves 7. Is she right?"*

✦ *"Let's read Alice's number sentence with the – sign. What does this sign mean?"*

✦ *"Tell me what happens to a number when you take some away. Does the number get bigger or smaller?"*

✦ *"7 take away 5 is 2. What happens if you put the 2 back again? So 7 count back 5 you land on 2 and if you count on 5 you get back to 7 again. You need to remember that counting on is the opposite of counting back."*

✦ *"What have you learned today?"*

✦ *"If I have 3 jam tarts, how many more would I need to give 7 children one each?"*

✦ LESSON TWO COUNTING BACK

✦ Assessment focus

Can the children understand counting back on a number line?

✦ Oral work and mental calculation

Mixed mental calculations

✦ *"Subtract 5 from 7. 10 take away 3. Which is more, 2 or 5? How many more? 4 and 5 more equals?"*

✦ *"Sam has 6 conkers and Kit has 3. How many do they have altogether? How many more conkers did Sam have than Kit?"*

✦ *"What is double 3/4/5, half of 4/6/8/10? Let's count from 3 up to 21 and back again. Now let's count in 2s from 3 up to 21 and back again. Let's count in 10s up to 100 and back again."*

✦ *"4 less than 11. 6 plus 5. How did you work that out?"*

✦ Starting point: whole class

✦ Round the large floor number line, do some counting back, making sure that all the children take a step to count the first number back. *"Stand on 6. Take 4 steps back, 1, 2, 3, 4. So 6 count back 4 means you land on 2. Do that counting back on your fingers. Hold up 6 fingers. Fold down 4. How many left standing? So what is 6 count back 4?"*

✦ To prepare children for the activity sheets, demonstrate how to show steps along a number line on the board. Give each pair a small number line and observe very closely as they do steps back with their fingers (or jump cubes representing the dolphins on the sheets). *"Stand on 8. Count/jump back 2. Where do you land?"*

✦ *"If I take 4 jumps back and I land on 3, which number did I start on?"*

✦ When you repeat the lesson, focus on 'how many more do I need to make … ?' Remember to write equations in a variety of ways, for example $\boxed{} - 3 = 7$.

Subtraction

◆ Group activities

Focus group

Do the starter activity again or move on to showing children how to find the difference between two numbers by either counting on, or counting back on a number line. Be clear that whether they count on or back, it is the same number of jumps.

Activity sheet 1: Make sure these children know how to draw in their jumps back. Read the number sentences with them.

Activity sheet 2: These children will use the – sign.

Activity sheet 3: This is a generic sheet and can be used both for counting on and counting back for children at any level. You can write in the numbers or ask children to choose numbers. You need to write 'Count back' or 'Count on'.

◆ Plenary

◆ With group 1, take one of their number sentences and write it on the board both as count back and

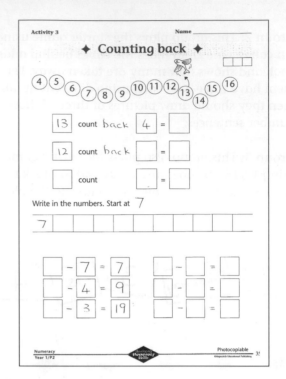

with the – sign. Ask all the children to read the number sentence and to do it on their fingers.

◆ *"What is the sign we use for subtraction/take away/ count back?"*

◆ *"What did you learn today about taking away and counting back?"*

◆ Further activities

◆ Use generic sheet 1 (page 90) and make spinners and use them to find differences. So if the children spin 4 on one spinner and 9 on the other, the difference is 5 so they move that many spaces. Race from the highest number on the sheet to the zero.

◆ Use generic sheet 2 (page 91) and make a subtraction game. Stick a large subtraction sign over the shark. Put numbers 15–7 on the octopus and 6–0 on the stingray (or to suit your children) and fill in the fishes with 1–9 randomly placed. They choose a number from the octopus, take away the number on the stingray then cover their number.

◆ Support

◆ Taking steps along the large floor number line each day with you just for two minutes can help children with one-to-one correspondence and with recalling number bonds.

◆ Use Activity sheet 3 to record more counting back with low numbers.

◆ Extension

◆ Use generic sheet 2 (page 91) to make a much harder subtraction game.

✦ Counting back ✦

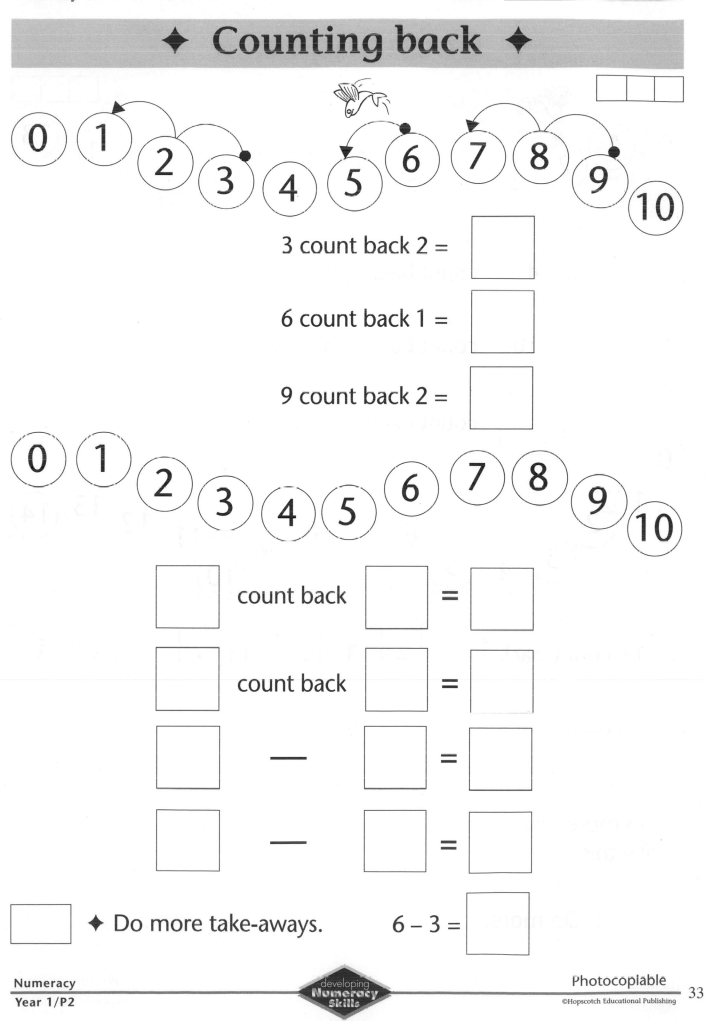

3 count back 2 =

6 count back 1 =

9 count back 2 =

□ count back □ = □

□ count back □ = □

□ — □ = □

□ — □ = □

□ ✦ Do more take-aways.   6 – 3 =

Name _____

✦ Counting back ✦

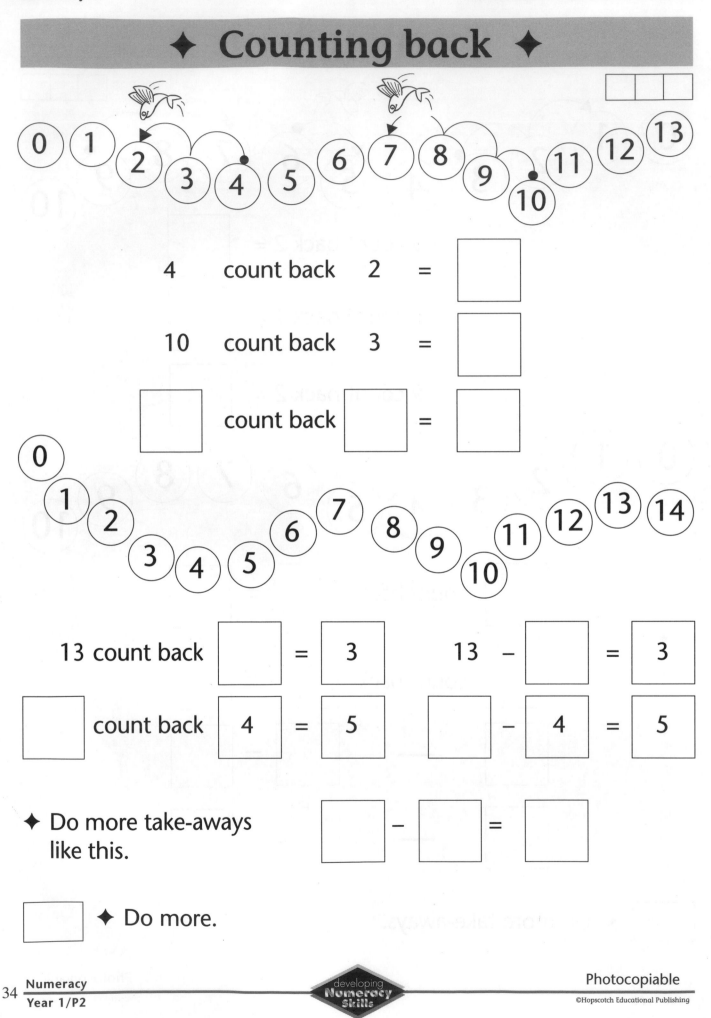

4   count back   2   =   ▢

10   count back   3   =   ▢

▢   count back   ▢   =   ▢

13 count back ▢ = 3   13 − ▢ = 3

▢ count back 4 = 5   ▢ − 4 = 5

✦ Do more take-aways like this.   ▢ − ▢ = ▢

▢   ✦ Do more.

Photocopiable

©Hopscotch Educational Publishing

◆ Counting back ◆

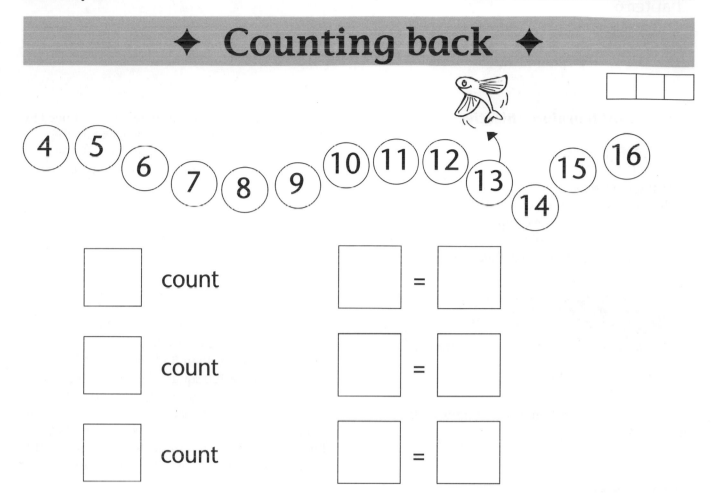

| 4 | 5 | 6 | 7 | 8 | 9 | 10 | 11 | 12 | 13 | 14 | 15 | 16 |

☐ count   ☐ = ☐

☐ count   ☐ = ☐

☐ count   ☐ = ☐

Write in the numbers. Start at

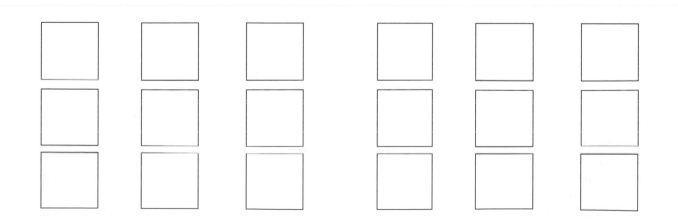

Photocopiable
©Hopscotch Educational Publishing

35

Calculation strategies 1

◆ Overall learning objectives

◆ Add 10 to single-digit numbers and count on in tens.
◆ Partition a 'teens' number into tens and units.
◆ Choose an appropriate calculating strategy for a range of numbers, for example identifying doubles and near-doubles.
◆ Know doubles to double 10 (then above).

◆◆ LESSON ONE SPLITTING NUMBERS ◆◆

◆ Assessment focus

Can the children partition a teens number into ten and ones?

◆ Resources

◆ large 100 square
◆ number lines
◆ several sets of number cards 0–9 and 11–19
◆ ten rods and ones (such as Cuisenaire)
◆ Unifix cubes
◆ an abacus
◆ tens and units cards
◆ paper bags of 10 'sweets' and single 'sweets'

◆ Oral work and mental calculation

Addition

◆ Play 'I'm giving you a present'. Each child starts with 10 teddies or cubes (the same number for everyone) and, taking turns around the circle, gives some of their teddies to the child next to them. *"Zach, I'm giving you 5 of my teddies. How many have you got now?"* They count Zach's teddies together and ask everyone if they agree with them. *"So Zach started with 10 and now he has 5 more. Do you all make that 15?"* Vary the game by throwing a dice to decide how many teddies are given. Make the teaching point that if a child

starts with 10 and is given more, we don't need to count that 10 again. Another day, extend the game to include the subtractions as well. *"Ben started with 10 and he gave Zach 5, so how many does Ben have left?"*

◆ Starting point: whole class

◆ Choose a single-digit number (such as 3) and hold up the 3 number card. Ask a child to the front to hold up 3 fingers and another to hold up 10 fingers. Count all the fingers and write the number (13) on the board. Repeat this with different numbers, then find each of the 'teen' numbers on the 100 square. Show how they are all in the second row and are made up of one ten and some ones. Demonstrate 'teen' numbers with ten rods, with an abacus, Unifix cubes and with bags of 10 'sweets' and single 'sweets'. Split 13/14/15 into the units/ones and the ten. *"Fifteen is made up of one ten and five units."*

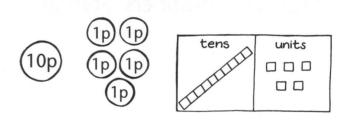

◆ Group activities

           Focus group

First, assess how well individual children can add 10 to a single-digit number. When all children have added 10 to some numbers, give children number cards (either the whole set 11–19 or just a few) and they work in pairs using ten rods and ones to make their numbers, telling you how they split numbers into tens and units. (Some children will be able to do 11 to 19 or 20 in order.)

36
©Hopscotch Educational Publishing

developing
Numeracy
Skills

Numeracy
Year 1/P2

Calculation strategies 1

 Teacher-independent groups

Group 1: Give these children number cards to suit their experience, and ask them to count out the right number of teddies/cubes and put them with the right number cards on a tray in a row in order to check at review time.

Group 2: Working in pairs, using the 'teen' number cards, this group should put out the numbers with Unifix cubes, making a 'ten train' all in one colour and the units in another, and do the same number on an abacus, in the order 11–19.

Group 3: Each child chooses a 'teen' number and represents it in as many different ways as they can, for example 15p, 15 on an abacus, 15 in Cuisenaire

✦ ✦ ✦ ✦ ✦ ✦

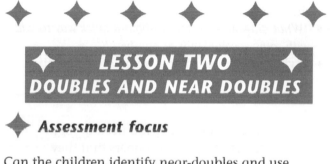

LESSON TWO
DOUBLES AND NEAR DOUBLES

✦ Assessment focus

Can the children identify near-doubles and use known double to calculate?

✦ Resources

✦ number line
✦ dominoes
✦ number cards

✦ Oral work and mental calculation

Doubles and near-doubles

✦ Teach children all the doubles first, up to double 5 using fingers, then to double 10. Play the 'doubles ping pong' game. You say *"ping"* and the class must reply *"pong"*. Then you say a number and they have to reply with the double, for example '4' '8'. Then say *"ping"* and the children reply *"pong"*, and follow this by saying another number

rods, a 10g mass and five 1g, a bag of 10 'sweets' and five more 'sweets'.

✦ Plenary session

✦ Ask group 1 to tell you their numbers. Check their counting by asking them to count their objects carefully. Note who needs more help with moving and counting objects.
✦ When all the 'ten trains' have been checked from group 2, tape them round with sticky tape and keep them in a container called 'ten trains' for mental maths time and for learning to count larger numbers beyond 20.
✦ Ask group 3 to show their numbers and to demonstrate splitting a number into a ten and units. *"How would you split 24 into tens and units?"*

✦ ✦ ✦ ✦ ✦ ✦

they have to double. Gradually increase the speed, but try to keep all the children with you. Keep repeating this activity to develop confidence with doubles. Then extend the game to halving.

✦ Starting point: whole class

✦ Write the calculations for doubles on paper, for example 4 + 4 = 8. Draw a domino pattern next to it. Show how to identify a 'near-double' with number cards that are next to each other, such as 4 and 5, and again draw this with domino patterns. Then show how you can use doubles they know to add near-doubles, so to add 4 + 5, they can double 4 to make 8 and just add one more. Demonstrate this on a number line.

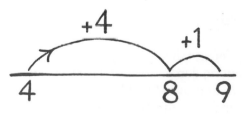

✦ Display the doubles alongside the near-doubles, for example 6 + 6 with 6 + 7 and 7 + 6.

Calculation strategies 1

◆ Group activities

Focus group

Assess which doubles these children know by asking for quick mental recall of them. Teach more doubles (extending some children to double 20, 30, 40 and 50). Identify near-doubles to suit the experience of the group by getting them to put number cards, such as 7 and 8, next to each other. Show them which calculations you *wouldn't* do by near-doubling, such as 8 + 1.

Teacher-independent groups

Use the photocopiable activity sheets

Activity sheet 1: Give this group a set of dominoes. They should identify the doubles and tick them, then work out near-doubles up to double 4.

Activity 2: These children should identify and tick both the doubles and near-doubles, then calculate the near-doubles. They need to know or work out the doubles of 10 and 11.

Activity 3: These children need to know or be able to work out the doubles up to 12, double 20 and 50, then choose their own. You can suggest numbers for the largest near-double, but encourage them to tell you the largest number they know first.

◆ Plenary session

✦ Let the children demonstrate their additions and tell you which numbers they ticked as doubles and near-doubles.
✦ Groups 2 and 3 can tell everyone which numbers they chose.
✦ *"What did you learn today about a quick way to add with some special kinds of numbers?"*
✦ Review individual targets involving calculations.

◆ Further activities

✦ At mental maths time gradually give experience of doubles up to double 20 for everyone and keep drawing children's attention to using doubles as a quick way of adding some numbers.

◆ Extension

✦ Split up numbers over 20 into tens and units and give them some harder calculations to do any way they want, such as '24 add 37'.

◆ Support

✦ Use generic sheet 2 (page 91) to make a doubling game. Cover the octopus and the shark and write 'double' there instead. Put numbers to suit your children on the stingray. The children work in pairs and take turns to choose a number from the stingray and double it, then cover the number they make

with their colour-counter. You need to fill in the fishes with the even numbers that they will make by doubling. The winner is the first to get three of their coloured counters in a row in any direction.

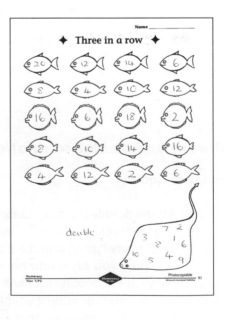

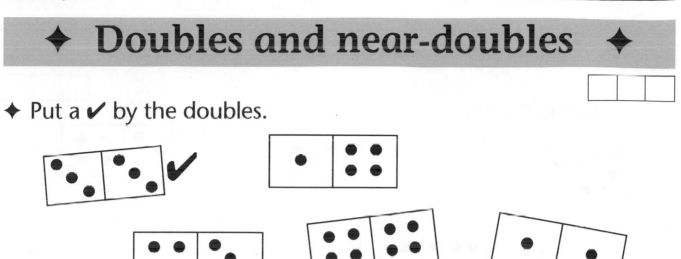

✦ Doubles and near-doubles ✦

✦ Put a ✔ by the doubles.

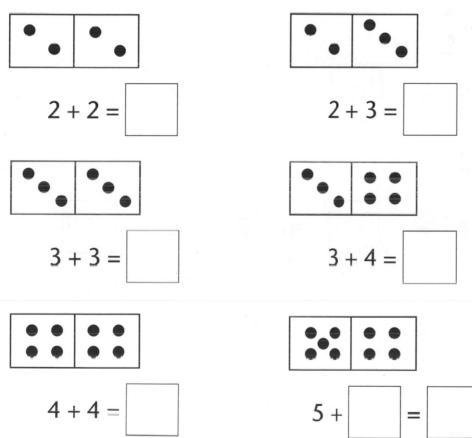

✦ Now do near-doubles.

2 + 2 = ☐

2 + 3 = ☐

3 + 3 = ☐

3 + 4 = ☐

4 + 4 = ☐

5 + ☐ = ☐

Draw some more near-doubles.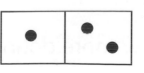

✦ Doubles and near-doubles ✦

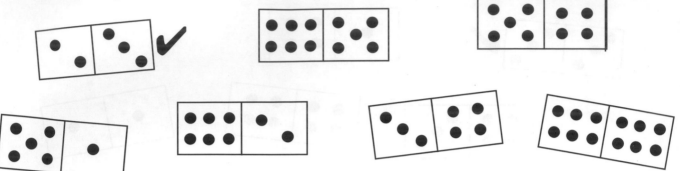

✦ Put a ✔ by the doubles and near-doubles.

✦ Now do these.

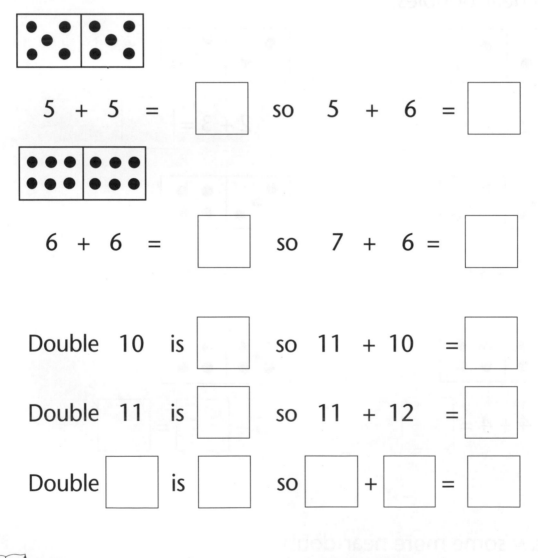

5 + 5 = ☐   so   5 + 6 = ☐

6 + 6 = ☐   so   7 + 6 = ☐

Double 10 is ☐   so 11 + 10 = ☐

Double 11 is ☐   so 11 + 12 = ☐

Double ☐ is ☐   so ☐ + ☐ = ☐

Draw more doubles and near-doubles.

developing
Numeracy
Skills

✦ Doubles and near-doubles ✦

✦ Put a ✔ by the doubles and near-doubles.

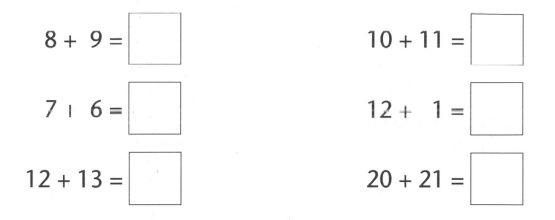

8 + 9 = ☐   10 + 11 = ☐

7 ⊦ 6 = ☐   12 + 1 = ☐

12 + 13 = ☐   20 + 21 = ☐

✦ Use number cards to help you write more near-doubles.

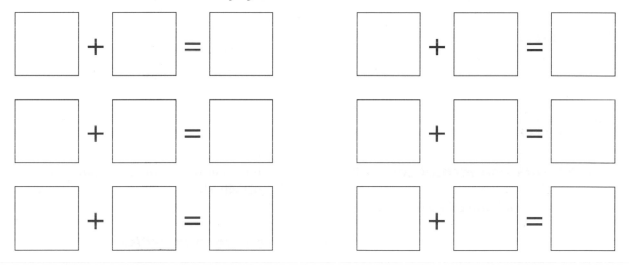

☐ + ☐ = ☐   ☐ + ☐ = ☐

☐ + ☐ = ☐   ☐ + ☐ = ☐

☐ + ☐ = ☐   ☐ + ☐ = ☐

✦ The largest near-double I can do is:

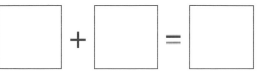

☐ + ☐ = ☐

Write more near-doubles.

Photocoplable
©Hopscotch Educational Publishing

Calculation strategies 2

 Overall learning objectives

- Partition into '5 and a bit' and recombine.
- Choose an appropriate calculating strategy for a range of numbers, for example putting the larger number first, and adding 9 by adding 10 and subtracting 1.

 **LESSON ONE CHANGE IT AROUND**

Assessment focus

Can the children see that putting the larger number first can speed up calculating?

Resources

- number lines
- cubes
- boards/trays
- stamper pens

Oral work and mental calculation

Hold 5 in their head and add a bit more

- Add numbers up to 10 using fingers, always using all five fingers on one hand. Ask *"what is this number?"*, holding up your fingers. Observe carefully which children want to start from 1 again. *"This is still 5 on this hand, isn't it? No-one crept in and chopped one of my fingers off, did they? So we don't need to count this 5 again. It is still 5. Hold it in your head and count on the extra fingers."*
- Keep demonstrating 5 and a bit numbers with fingers up to 10, both in order and out of order, so that most children know all the numbers and can respond fairly quickly with answers.

Starting point: whole class

- Demonstrate how counting on 1 plus 10 in ones takes ages. But if we put the larger number first and hold that 10 in our head, we just add on 1 on our fingers. (Note who still wants to count the 10 all the way from 1.)

"Which is quicker, 9 add 2 or 2 add 9?"

- Demonstrate writing calculations such as 1 + 8 the other way round in preparation for the activity sheets.

Group activities

 Focus group

Work with this group to assess who understands how to put the larger number first. Make sure the children understand which is the larger number by ordering number cards, then use the cards to make number sentences with the larger number first, for example '10 add 2 more'.

Calculation strategies 2

 Teacher-independent groups

Use the photocopiable activity sheets.

Activity sheet 1: For this sheet children just need to add the two numbers and relate 'and' to the + sign. The larger number is already put first in the examples. Give them stamper pens (made by Crayola and available in high-street shops) for the blank example – but don't be too surprised if they don't stamp the larger number first!

Activity sheet 2: These children should reverse the numbers then do the calculations. Remind them to hold the larger number in their head.

Activity sheet 3: This gives practice with putting the larger numbers first and some other calculations for you to ask *"How did you do that?"*

◆ **Plenary session**

✦ Go through the group 1 additions, asking the children to show you how they did them. Demonstrate how they can hold the first number in their head and count on with their fingers. (Some children are likely to need more practice with adding small numbers before they see the need to put the larger number first and why this is quicker.)

✦ Group 2 children can show how they put the larger number first.

✦ Group 3 children can share their methods for doing the calculations on the lower part of their sheet.

✦ *"So we use lots of different ways to add numbers. The way we choose depends on the numbers, so we probably wouldn't do 7+8 by putting the larger number first, we would probably double the 7 and add 1."* (See Further activities on the next page.)

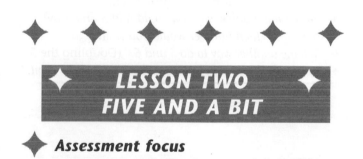

LESSON TWO
FIVE AND A BIT

◆ **Assessment focus**

Can the children split numbers into '5 and a bit' to aid calculating, and then recombine them?

◆ **Resources**

✦ number line

◆ **Oral work and mental calculation**

Adding 9 by adding 10 first

✦ When children are reasonably secure with showing jumps of 10 along a number line and with adding 10 to numbers, you can move on to adding 9 by adding 10 first, then jumping back 1. Have a number line on display and show the

jump of 10, then the one going back the other way. *"So if 5 add 10 is 15, 5 add 9 is one less than 15."*

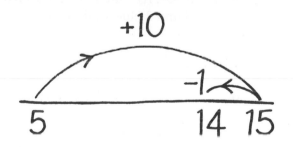

◆ **Starting point: whole class**

✦ Demonstrate how we can split up numbers like 7 and 9 into 5 and a bit. Do this with cubes, always keeping the 5 in the same colour.

✦ Then demonstrate adding with 5 and a bit, at first having one of the numbers as 5 each time, for example 5 + 7 and 5 + 9. Show how the numbers can be split up making two lots of five each time and then adding on the extra bit. If the children

Calculation strategies 2

can manage it, move on to choosing numbers where both numbers have to be split into 5 and a bit, combining first the two 5s, then the two extra bits.

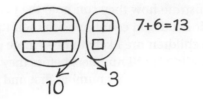

$$7 + 6 = 13$$

10   3

"7 splits into 5 and 2. 6 splits into 5 and 1. Then put the two 5s together to make 10. Then we need to add the 2 and the 1."

◆ Group activities

Focus group

Repeat the starting activity at a level suitable for the group. (You will need to repeat additions with 6, 7, 8 and 9 by splitting into 5 and a bit daily at mental maths time for a few weeks.)

Teacher independent groups

Group 1: These children make the numbers 5 to 10 by making each 5 in, say, red cubes, then 6 is 5 red and 1 blue, 7 is 5 red and 2 blue, and so on.

Group 2: Give calculations such as 5 + 6 and 5 + 7 on paper or on the board, (using 5 as the starting number each time) and ask the children to lay that out in cubes on the board, each time making all the 5s in one colour, such as red, and splitting the second number into a red 5 and some blue. Ask them to draw and colour what they do.

Group 3: Give calculations such as 6 + 7 and 8 + 9 and do the same as group 2, laying out the cubes on a tray, and again, splitting each number into 5 and a bit. The children draw what they do and write the answer to the calculation.

◆ Plenary session

◆ Let group 1 children show their 5 and bit, and demonstrate each number with five fingers and some more fingers.
◆ Groups 2 and 3 show their drawings of splitting 5 and a bit, then recombining them.
◆ *"So tell me a quick way you could add 5 and 6 by splitting. Which number would you split?"*
◆ *"Tell me another way to do 5 and 6."* (Doubling the 5.)
◆ *"Work out 5 add 9 by splitting the 9 into 5 and a bit."*

◆ Further activities

◆ Present a range of different calculations to children and ask them how they might do them. Include numbers that can be done by putting the larger number first, using doubles and near-doubles, adding 9 by adding 10 and subtracting 1, splitting numbers into 5 and a bit and recombining.

1 + 12	3 + 11	2 + 10	2 + 9
11 + 9	5 + 6	7 + 8	6 + 8

How would you do these?

◆ Extension

◆ Give more experience of bridging through 10, for example 6 + 5, and later 20, by adding mentally numbers such as 15 and 6, 17 and 8.

◆ Support

◆ Give more experience with making cubes/ beads and so on as '5 and a bit' using two colours as above. Give more practice physically splitting the fives and combining them to make a ten train and then combining the bits. You might need to repeat this many times.

44
©Hopscotch Educational Publishing

developing
Numeracy
Skills

Numeracy
Year 1/P2

✦ Add some more ✦

| 5 | and | | more is | |

| | and | | more is | |

☐ + ☐ = ☐   ☐ + ☐ = ☐

✏️ Draw

| | and | | more is | |

☐ + ☐ = ☐

📖 Draw more.

✦ Add big numbers ✦

✦ Put the larger number first.

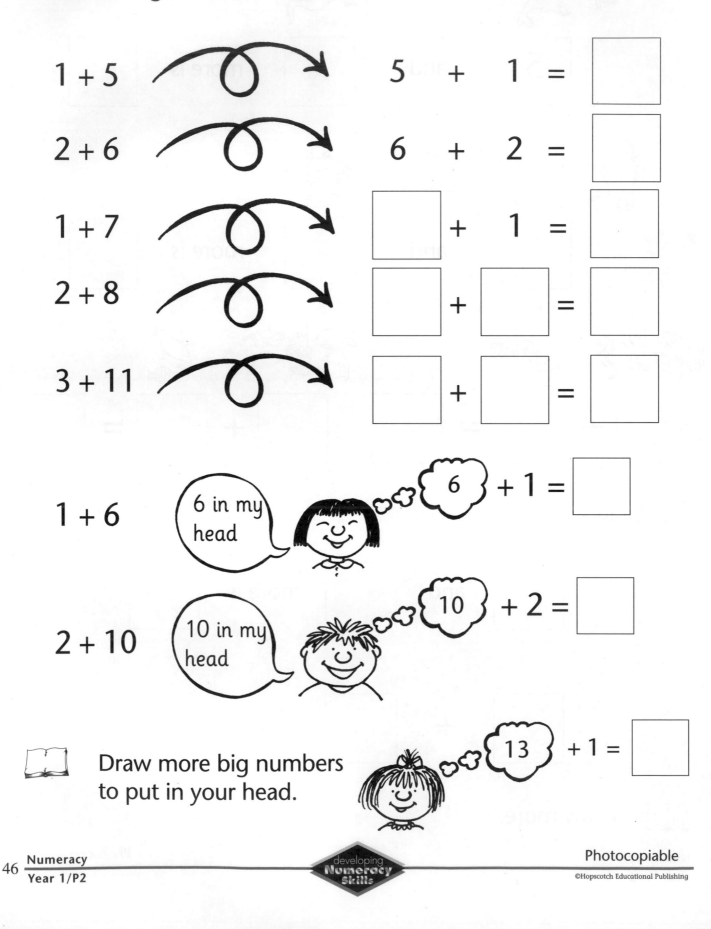

1 + 5   5   +   1   =

2 + 6   6   +   2   =

1 + 7   ☐   +   1   =

2 + 8   ☐   +   ☐   =

3 + 11   ☐   +   ☐   =

1 + 6   6 in my head   6 + 1 = ☐

2 + 10   10 in my head   10 + 2 = ☐

📖 Draw more big numbers to put in your head.   13 + 1 = ☐

developing
Numeracy
Skills

◆ Numbers in my head ◆

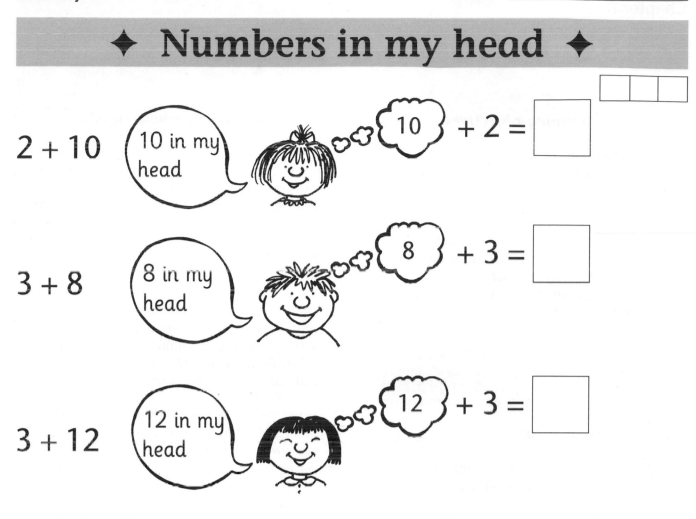

$2 + 10$

10 in my head

$10 + 2 = \boxed{}$

$3 + 8$

8 in my head

$8 + 3 = \boxed{}$

$3 + 12$

12 in my head

$12 + 3 = \boxed{}$

◆ Tell your teacher how you did these.

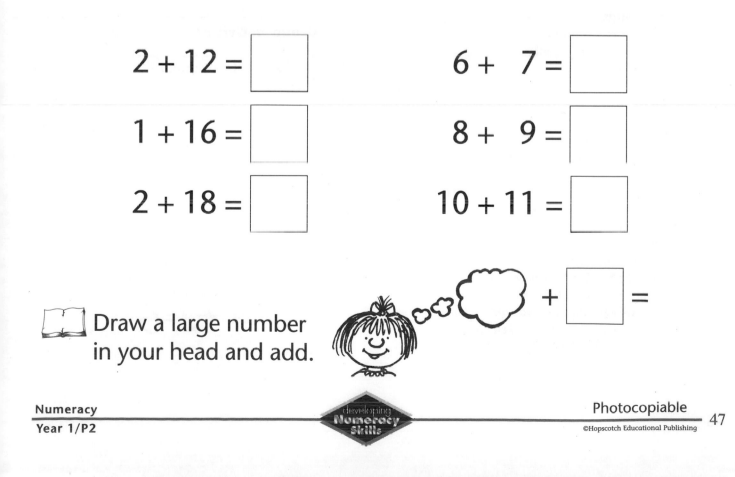

$2 + 12 = \boxed{}$ $6 + \ 7 = \boxed{}$

$1 + 16 = \boxed{}$ $8 + \ 9 = \boxed{}$

$2 + 18 = \boxed{}$ $10 + 11 = \boxed{}$

📖 Draw a large number in your head and add.

$+ \boxed{} = $

Photocopiable
©Hopscotch Educational Publishing

47

Number stories and puzzles

◆ Overall learning objectives

- ✦ Make decisions by choosing and using appropriate operations and mental strategies to solve number problems.
- ✦ Solve simple mathematical problems or puzzles with numbers and shapes.
- ✦ Explain methods and reasoning orally.
- ✦ Solve real-life problems by counting, addition, subtraction, halving or doubling.
- ✦ Begin to bridge through 10 and later 20, when adding a single-digit number.

◆ LESSON ONE NUMBER STORIES

◆ Assessment focus

Can the children choose and use appropriate operations and mental strategies to solve number problems?

◆ Resources

- ✦ number cards
- ✦ symbol cards +, – and =
- ✦ play people and equipment

◆ Oral work and mental calculation

Real-life problems using counting, addition, subtraction, halving or doubling.

- ✦ *"How much is 3p and 2p and 1p?"* (Give children plenty of opportunity to handle real money to develop their coin recognition.) Add up how many marbles if Tony has 2, 3 and 8. Remember to put the larger number first to make it easier. *"What is half of 20p?"* *"Chews cost 5p each. How much for 2?"* *"We have 34 pencils in the pot. How many if we take one out? Two out?"* *"Half of the bean bags in this crate have been taken out. 10 are left. How many were taken out?"*

◆ Starting point: whole class

- ✦ Make up stories that need addition and subtraction, for example *"There were 5 fish and then 5 more came along. Tell me how many fish altogether. How did you do that? So Mina, you added 5 and another 5 on your fingers. Tricia said she knew double 5 was 10."* Write the calculation on the board using both words and symbols.
- ✦ Do some subtraction stories, for example *"Gita had 18 sweets and she ate 7. How many did she have left?"* Write these calculations on the board and point out the – sign. Then move on with some more problems that children can make sense of (set them in the context of money, or your class topic, or with fish and so on). For example, *"There were 18 fish playing round the rocks and 3 swam away."* Write the 18 on the board and ask the children what to write next. Establish that it was a take-away calculation.
- ✦ Use repeated addition, counting in 2s, 5s and 10s, for example *"2 socks and another 2 and another 2"*. Begin to bridge through 10 and later 20, when adding a single-digit number to a 'teens' number, for example *"There were 14 dolphins and 7 more came to play, how many altogether?"*

◆ Group activities

Focus group

Make a simple sheet with three spaces so that the children can draw their numbers stories like a cartoon strip. They should tell their stories first, establish which are adding and which are subtraction, then you can write all the calculations on the board.

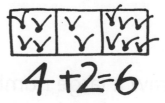

Number stories and puzzles

Teacher-independent groups

Group 1: Provide play people and equipment and number cards and ask these chidren to make up a number story ready for the plenary session. They must select the number cards they need.

Group 2: Use the same sheet as for the focus group and choose some numbers for them, for example 'teen' numbers. They must write their number sentence and, if they can write reasonably quickly, they could write out their story as well for a class book, 'Our book of number stories'.

Group 3: Let these children draw their own comic strips and make up one subtraction and one adding 'sum'. Suggest some challenging numbers and remind them that you will ask them *how* they did their calculations in their head.

✦ Plenary session

✦ There will not be time for every child to tell their story, so extend this session into the next day, with each child working out each calculation on their fingers (and toes or in pairs for larger numbers) and talking about each number sentence and the appropriate signs. Establish that the – sign means 'balances' or 'equals' or 'altogether makes' and make some equations:

$$12 + 4 = 16$$
$$12 + \square = 16$$
$$16 = 12 + \square$$
$$16 - \square = 12$$

✦ *"How did you work that out? Did you remember to put the larger number first?"*
✦ *"When we work on number stories we must think carefully about when we need to add and when we take away."*

◆ ◆ ◆ ◆ ◆ ◆   ◆ ◆ ◆ ◆ ◆ ◆

LESSON TWO
PUZZLES

✦ Assessment focus

Can the children solve simple mathematical puzzles with numbers and shape and explain methods and reasoning orally?

✦ Resources

✦ large cards, 3 each of 1p, 2p, and 3p
✦ two large dice
✦ 2D shapes
✦ paper fish

✦ Oral work and mental calculation

Puzzles with dice

✦ Throw two dice of two different colours and add up the numbers. Repeat this several times. Ask *"How can I make a score of 6?"* (1 and 5, 2 and 4, 3 and 3 and so on. Note that with two different

colours of dice, red 4 and blue 2 is different from blue 4 and red 2.)
✦ Extend the tasks each time you do this, for example *"How many ways are there of making 12?"* (Just one way, 6 and 6.) What about ways to make 7? (6 and 1, 5 and 2, 4 and 3, 3 and 4, 2 and 5, 1 and 6.)

✦ Starting point: whole class

✦ Lay out a 3-by-3 lattice as on Activity sheet 1 and ask the children to help you to put six fish in every row and every column. Each row and column, as well as the diagonal lines, must add up to 6. Here is one way to do it.

Chapter 8

Number stories and puzzles

◆ Talk about the pattern and check by adding each row carefully, making sure the children understand 'row', 'column' and 'diagonal.'

◆ Then do the puzzle again, but in a slightly more abstract way just with cards 1p to 3p. Help the children to make connections with what they have just done with fish, but point out that there is more than one way to do this puzzle.

◆ Use 2D shapes to introduce the tasks in Activity sheets 2 and 3, this time putting one of each shape in each line. (Make sure the children can distinguish each shape as 'with 3 sides' and so on).

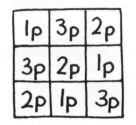 

◆ Group activities

  Focus group

Do one of the puzzles with this group (with an able group you could try the 4-by-4 shape puzzle in Activity sheet 3 but start with a completely blank grid). Or choose a different puzzle, for example ways to score 7 with two dice.

 Teacher-independent groups

Use the photocopiable activity sheets.

Activity sheet 1: This is a repeat of the starter activity. The children should draw fish in the squares. Focus on adding up to 6 each time.

Activity sheet 2: On this sheet, the first activity is the same as the whole class starter but using numbers. Then the children do the same activity but using shapes. They cut out and place the shapes and check with a partner before sticking them. (There is more than one way to do it.)

Activity sheet 3: These children write in the numbers 1, 2 and 3 on the top square. No help is given them with this part. They cut and stick on the lower square where some help is given.

◆ Plenary session

◆ Encourage each group to explain their methods and reasoning. Try to find different ways of solving the same puzzle.

◆ "How do you know it must be a 2 in that space?"

◆ "Who found a different way to do it?'

◆ Further activities

◆ Make a magic square with other numbers. These don't add up to the same number along the diagonal and some numbers are repeated in the same rows.

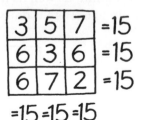

◆ Extension

◆ Give the children a magic square adding up to 20. Give it with several numbers missing.

 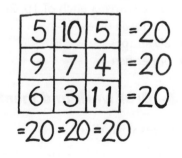

◆ Support

◆ Let the children solve the problems in pairs. SEN children need challenges too.

✦ A fish puzzle ✦

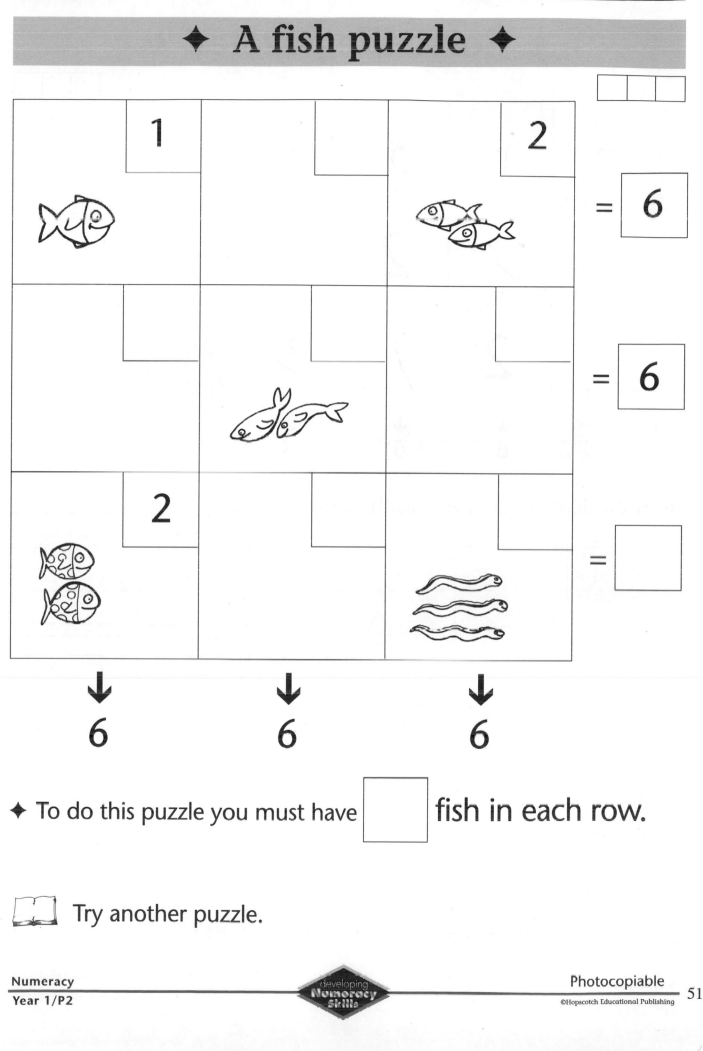

✦ To do this puzzle you must have ☐ fish in each row.

📖 Try another puzzle.

✦ Solve the puzzles ✦

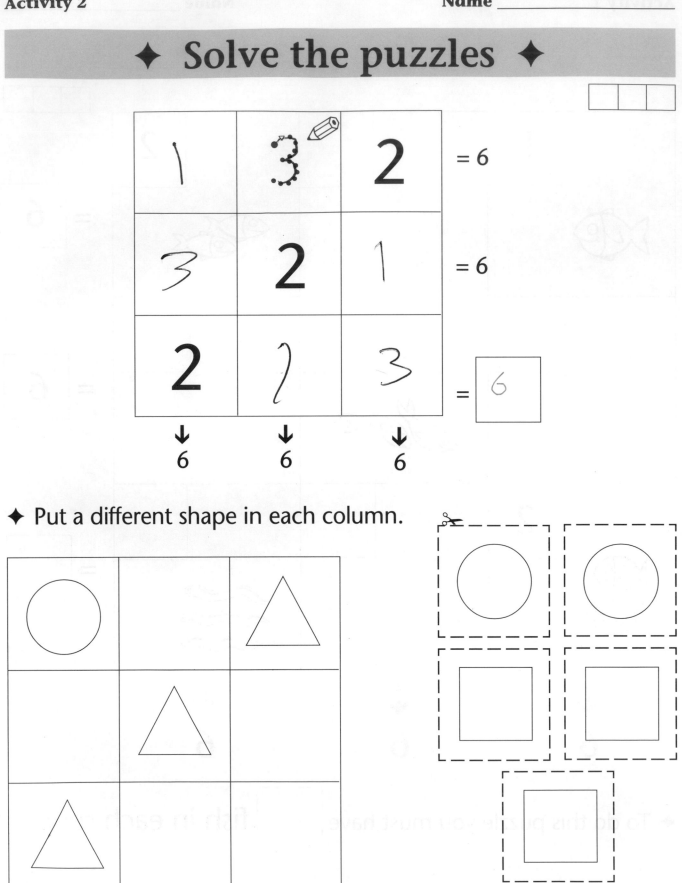

1	3	2	= 6
3	2	1	= 6
2	2	3	= 6

= 6

↓ 6   ↓ 6   ↓ 6

✦ Put a different shape in each column.

Is there more than one way to solve these?

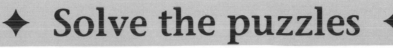

◆ Solve the puzzles ◆

◆ Write 1, 2 or 3 in each row.

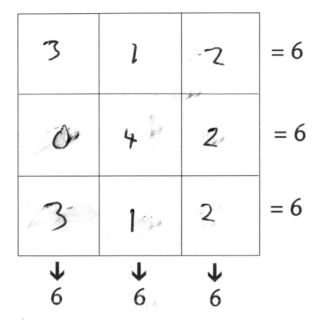

3	1	2	= 6
0	4	2	= 6
3	1	2	= 6

↓   ↓   ↓
6   6   6

◆ Put 1 of each shape in each row and column.

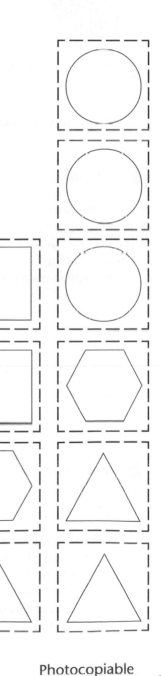

Money

◆ Overall learning objectives

✦ Solve simple mathematical problems using own strategies.
✦ Explain methods and reasoning.
✦ Recognise coins of different values.
✦ Give change to 10/20p.
✦ Pay an exact sum of money with a variety of coins.

✦ LESSON ONE ✦ COIN RECOGNITION

◆ Assessment focus

Can the children recognise all coins and add up small amounts of money?

◆ Resources

✦ real and plastic money
✦ a table-top shop
✦ packets of fish food and so on for the shop (these could be of various weights and sizes so they could also be used for Chapter 11)

◆ Oral work and mental calculation

Money

✦ Sing '5 currant buns in a baker's shop' with the children paying 1p for each bun. Change the rhyme a bit and let them buy two or three at a time with that many pennies. Role-play buying a bun with a 10p coin and the shopkeeper giving change.

◆ Starting point: whole class

✦ *"Today we are going to learn about the eight different coins we have in our country. Who knows the name of a coin and what it looks like?"* Have a pot of money (real is best) and ask some children to the front to pick out a coin that they know. Hold up the eight different coins and describe them. *"This 2p is the largest brown one."* Roughly draw the coins on the board, writing the amount inside them as the children will need to for recording their work.
✦ Have a few items for sale. (If you don't have space to set up a larger class shop, use a table top.)
✦ *"Tubes of sweets cost 4p. Come and find 4 pennies to pay for it. How much would two tubes cost? How did you work that out?"* (Remind the children about doubling and go over doubles up to double 10.)
✦ *"Fish food is 5p a packet. How could you pay for that with just one coin/with more than one coin/with no change? Dolphin food is 7p a packet. How could you pay for that with no change?"* (Lay out the different ways to pay, as on Activity sheet 1.)

◆ Group activities

 Focus group

Make sure all the children can recognise all the coins. Make up amounts with coins, for example finding lots of different ways to pay 8p with no change. With more able children you could move on to giving change from 10p. Some children will need repeated practice with this.

 Teacher independent groups

Use the photocopiable activity sheets.

Activity sheet 1: These children should draw around the eight different coins, then make 5p in two ways, again drawing round the coins. Some of them might find this second part too difficult, so let them draw around five 1p coins in one purse, and you put two 2p and a 1p in the second purse. Give them practice with different coins to make 5p over the next few weeks.

54
©Hopscotch Educational Publishing

developing
Numeracy
Skills

Numeracy
Year 1/P2

Money

Activity sheet 2: These children should match the coin to the money amount, then find four ways to pay out 7p with no change.

Activity sheet 3: These children should find four ways to pay out 13p with no change.

◆ Plenary session

◆ "Who can tell me how many different coins we have?" (8.) Group 1 children can hold up the eight

different coins. Let them demonstrate how to pay for a 5p pack of fish food. "So this one 5p coin has the same value as those five 1p coins." (Many children find this a very difficult concept and will need plenty of practice with making up amounts of money.)

◆ Other groups show their amounts of money. Ask all of them to check the amounts with their fingers. "One 5p add another 2p. How much? How did you work that out?"

◆ "Tell me what you learned about money today."

LESSON TWO
GIVING CHANGE

◆ Assessment focus

Can the children give change to 10/20p?

◆ Resources

◆ real and plastic money

◆ Oral work and mental calculation

Calculating money amounts

◆ "Lisa spent 1p and 3p and 4p. How much altogether? How did you work that out?"

◆ "What would it cost to buy 2 apples at 4p each? How much change from 10p? How did you work that out?"

◆ "Chews cost 2p each. How many could you buy for a 5p coin? Would you get any change? How many could you buy for a 10p coin? Would you get change? How many could you buy for 12p? Which 2 coins could pay 12p exactly? Tell me another way to pay 12p with more than 2 coins. Is there another way?"

◆ Starting point: whole class

◆ "Today we are going to learn about how to give change. So if Tony had a 10p coin and he wanted to buy one packet of fish food for 5p, the shopkeeper would need to give him some change." (Beware! Some children who see their parents shop in supermarkets with a card have no idea what 'giving change' means! They need to practise this in the class shop.)

◆ "Lucy has a 10p coin. Does she have enough to buy an 8p bun? How much change would she get? Tell us how you worked that out."

◆ Give each pair of children some coins and go around the circle with each pair buying things from you. All the children should try to do the calculations.

◆ You could also give each pair 10p and go round asking them to select something that they can buy that also means they must have change.

◆ Give help with doubles, for example two buns at 8p each.

◆ Practise larger but fairly straightforward amounts when the children are ready. For example, "Clare has a £1 coin. How many 10p lollies could she buy?"

Money

◆ Group activities

Focus group

Work out amounts of change from 10p. You could have 9 items ranging from 1p to 9p. Ask the children to explain to you how they worked it out. What if you had 20p? How much change would you get? With children who need lots of support, check that they can recognise all the coins and keep practising making up money amounts with several different coins. Let them play at giving change. Show them how to work out amounts adding on their fingers.

Teacher-independent groups

Group 1: Draw four or five purses on some paper and give these children an amount of money to make in each one with different coins, such as 6p. If this is too hard for some, let them draw around 1p coins for small amounts as on Activity sheet 1 in Chapter 10.

Group 2: Give these children 10p to spend on items from the shop and let them draw what they buy and work out their change.

Group 3: These children do the same as group 2 but with 20p.

◆ Plenary session

◆ Let each group demonstrate their amounts and how much change. Emphasise that you get change when you give the shopkeeper more money than the cost of what you are buying. *"Katie has 10p and the chocolate cost 7p. Is 7 more or less than 10? So will she get change?"*
◆ *"What have you learned today about giving change?"*
◆ You might want to identify children who would need to have some aspect of money as one of their targets for the next half-term.
◆ Involve parents, perhaps by setting a 'homework' activity where the child counts money in an adult's purse once a week for half a term.

◆ Further activities

◆ Have a class fruit shop for a couple of weeks at break time selling slices of banana and quarters of apples for a few pence.
◆ Ask parents to let children count the coins in their purse once a week.

◆ Extension

◆ Let the children make a shopping list of some items to buy if they had 50p or £1.
◆ Able children can take the role of shopkeeper to show others how to give change.

◆ Support

◆ Let the children practise putting out coins to make 4p/5p/6p and make a display of these to copy.
◆ At odd moments, do more coin recognition and keep emphasising five 1p coins has the same value as one 5p coin.

✦ Coins ✦

✦ Draw round these coins.

1p	2p	5p
10p	20p	50p
£1	£2	

✦ How could you pay for 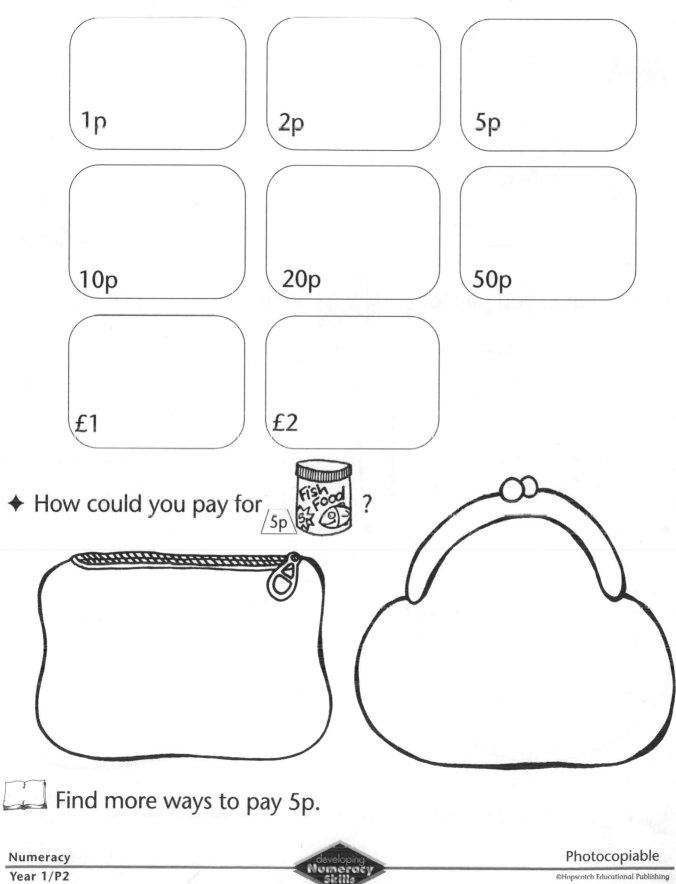 ?

📖 Find more ways to pay 5p.

✦ **Money** ✦

✦ Join the coins to the labels.

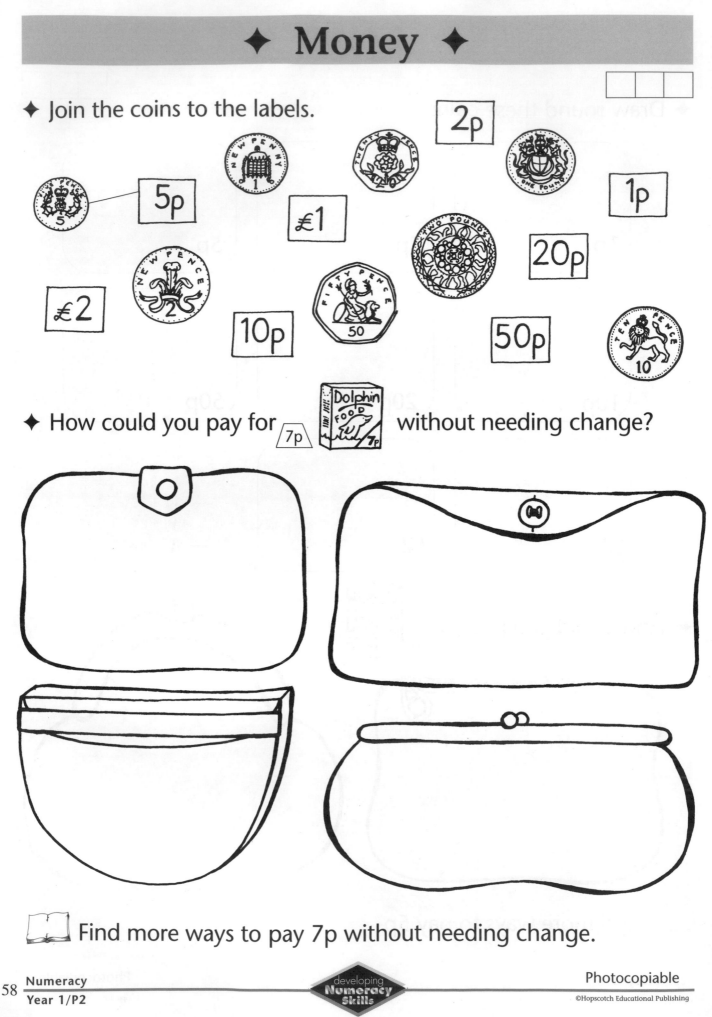

✦ How could you pay for [7p] without needing change?

📖 Find more ways to pay 7p without needing change.

Photocopiable

developing
Numeracy
Skills

✦ **Money** ✦

✦ Draw lots of different coins. Write how much.

2p

Special Curly
Seashells 13p

How can you pay
without needing
change?

Find more ways.

developing
Numeracy
Skills

Photocopiable
©Hopscotch Educational Publishing

59

Time and money

◆ Overall learning objectives

◆ Use own mental strategies to solve simple problems of time and money
◆ Solve simple real-life problems and puzzles of time and money.

✦ LESSON ONE
VISITING AN AQUARIUM

◆ Assessment focus

Can the children talk about the passage of time and read o'clock times?

◆ Resources

◆ analogue and digital alarm clocks
◆ timers
◆ large teaching clock
◆ plastic and real money

◆ Oral work and mental calculation

The passage of time and counting

◆ Try various counting tasks and time how long the children take in minutes and seconds. For example, *"Let's count in 2s all the way to 20 and then back again to 0"* or *"Let's count to 20 as fast as we can"* or *"Let's count to 100 in ones from 0"* or *"Let's count in 5s to 30"*. Teach the children to count in seconds, saying *"one second, two seconds, three seconds"* and so on.

◆ Starting point: whole class

◆ Sequence some events to give a sense of the passage of time in daily life. For example, *"The class shop and aquarium opens at 9.30, then we can buy things, then it shuts again at playtime at 10.30. At 12 noon we go to lunch."*
◆ Use a kitchen timer with a bell to set times for various parts of lessons, such as 10 minutes for an oral maths time.
◆ Use a large teaching clock to show o'clock and half-past and relate the long and short hands to a real clock. Link analogue time to a digital clock.
◆ Set up a role-play situation such as a class outing to an aquarium. *"We need to be at school at 8am so that we get to the aquarium at 9am when it opens."* Give the children the coins they need, a £1 coin for the entrance fee, a 5p coin to buy fish food, a 10p coin to buy a lolly and so on. Choose some children to take the entrance fee, and others to sell drinks and lollies and so on.

◆ Group activities

Focus group

Count the money taken in the role-play by various children. Set up other buying situations, such as *"How much change would you get from 10p if you bought an 8p bun?"*

Time and money

Teacher-independent groups

Use the photocopiable activity sheets.

Activity sheet 1: These children just draw around the correct number of 1p coins. Leave a clock on display saying 9am.

Activity sheet 2: These children draw in the hands of the clocks and can just draw round the appropriate coins. Some might be able to add up the money they spent, £2.70.

Activity sheet 3: Have a large clock on display with the numbers clearly visible. These children have to buy multiple packs of fish food and give change from 20p.

◆ Plenary session

◆ The focus group can show some totals of money.

◆ Let all the groups show their times on the clocks. Relate those times to the actual time on the class clock. *"It's almost 12 o'clock, so we just have a few more minutes."*

◆ Work with everyone on the group 3 tasks with 5p fish food, holding up sets of five fingers and counting in 5s. *"So 3 packs would cost 15p. How much change from 20p?"*

LESSON TWO
THREE-COIN PUZZLES

◆ Assessment focus

Can the children make up small amounts of money?

◆ Resources

◆ number cards 10, 20, 30 to 100, enough for each child to have two cards
◆ a stopwatch
◆ plastic and real money
◆ yoghurt pots and labels
◆ two cut-out shapes of a sea snake's head (see opposite)

◆ Oral work and mental calculation

Ordering multiples of 10

◆ You need number cards 10, 20, 30 to 100, enough for each child to have two cards and a stopwatch. Give out the cards then put down one or more sea snake's heads with 0 on them and start the stopwatch. Go around the circle, with the children taking turns to put down one card in order. So, if the first child has 10, they put that next to the snake's head. If the next child doesn't have 20, move quickly along to the next child who has. Play until one child has put down both of their cards, or until all the cards have been played, or for a quick game, until just one snake is completed.

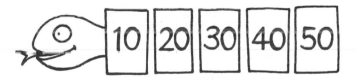

◆ Starting point: whole class

◆ Go through coin recognition again for those who need that experience. Have a pot of money in the centre of the circle and give everyone about six coins. Sitting the group 1 children close to you, ask the children, in pairs, to make up amounts of money, such as 4p made with two 2p coins. Let them use as many coins as they want, even totalling all their coins. (Let them put coins back in the pot in the middle of the circle and take out

Time and money

any other ones they need.) Go around the circle looking at amounts. For children who can manage it, ask them about giving change for 10p and 20p.

✦ Then introduce a special money puzzle where they can only use three coins that are all the same each time. They must see which amounts of money they can make, such as 3p with three pennies or 6p with three 2p coins. Go around the circle looking at the three coins and checking totals.

✦ *"Is it possible to make 10p with three of the same coins?"* (No.)

✦ *"What's the most you can make with three coins?"* (£6 with £2 coins.)

◆ Group activities

Focus group

Use this time to work with various groups at their own level of working with money. Some might still be struggling with coin recognition and most might still find giving change difficult, but try to get all children able to give change for 10p by the end of the year. Some children will need more help with understanding equivalent amounts, for example that five 1p coins have the same value as a 5p coin.

Teacher-independent groups

Group 1: Give amounts of money (stick labels on the side of yoghurt pots) to make with three coins but this time the coins can be mixed, for example 3p, 4p and 5p. (If this is too difficult for this group, let them play in the shop.)

Group 2: With 3 coins each time these children should make 4p (1, 1, 2); 5p (2, 2, 1); 6p (2, 2, 2); 7p (5, 1, 1); 8p (5, 2, 1) and 9p (5, 2, 2).

Group 3: With just three coins this group should make 8p (5, 2, 1); 9p (5, 2, 2); 11p (5, 5, 1); 12p (5, 5, 2 or 10, 1, 1); 13p (10, 2, 1); 14p (10, 2, 2) and 15p (5, 5, 5). *"Find some amounts you can't make."*

◆ Plenary session

✦ Sit the children who are struggling with coin recognition and equivalence near you so that they can help you to check the money. When amounts have been checked you might want to stick coins down on to card with sticky tape to make an interactive display.

✦ *"Show me how you worked out that is 7 pence."*

✦ *"Why did nobody make 10 pence?"* (You can't make that with three coins.)

◆ Further activities

✦ You will need to do more activities involving shopping and giving change. Do these as a whole class. For example, tell the children that goldfish cost 15p each, and they should work in pairs to find out the change needed from 20p. Relate this to finger counting. You can do this in odd moments – *"I've got a 2p coin and a 5p coin in my hand. Hold up that many fingers. Do I have enough to buy an ice-cream that costs 50p? Can I buy three 2p chews? Will I have some money left?"*

◆ Extension

✦ *"Which amounts of money can you make with three coins using 50p, £1 and £2 coins?"*

◆ Support

✦ Make up yoghurt pots with labels on them of amounts of money to make. Ideally use real money and enlist some parent help.

✦ Time and money ✦

The clock says

◻ o'clock

✦ Draw round coins.

Fish food 5p = ◻ p

Buns 8p = ◻ p

Drinks 20p = ◻ p

You need a ⊕ stamp.
Draw more clock times.

✦ Time and money ✦

✦ The aquarium opens at 9am. Draw the times on the clocks and the money in the purses.

9:00

Entrance Fee £1

£1

✦ Feed the sharks at 10am.

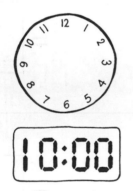

10:00

Shark Food 50p

50p

✦ Lunch time is 12 noon.

12:00

drinks 20p

sandwich £1

£1.20

✦ Draw more times.

developing
Numeracy
Skills

◆ Time and money ◆

◆ Write the clock numbers.

◆ Show **3:00** on the clock.

Meg has 10p

5p a pack

She can buy ☐ packs.

Tom has 20p. He wants 1 pack.

How much change from 20p? ☐ p

📖 How many packs for 🪙 ?

Measuring

◆ Overall learning objectives

◆ Understand and use the vocabulary of length, mass and capacity.
◆ Compare length, mass and capacity by direct comparison and by measuring with a range of non-standard and standard measures.
◆ Make rough estimates of length, mass and capacity and then measure with suitable units.
◆ Solve simple word problems explaining how the problem was solved.

◆◆ LESSON ONE LONGER AND SHORTER ◆

◆ Assessment focus

Can the children compare lengths and use appropriate standard and non-standard units of measurement?

◆ Resources

◆ string
◆ stick glue
◆ scissors
◆ a variety of paper fish
◆ lots of cubes

◆ Oral work and mental calculation

Choosing suitable ways of measuring

◆ *"What could you measure using a ruler/garden canes/ a litre jug/scales/a piece of string?"*
◆ *"If I wanted to weigh this parcel to see how heavy it is, would I put this garden cane next to it like this? Look, it is shorter than the garden cane. Do I know how heavy it is now?"*
◆ *"Would I measure enough drink for everyone in the class using this ruler?"*
◆ *"Tell me something that could help you to find how long your foot is. How could we work out if Ruth is taller or shorter than Yasmeen? How could we find out*

if this jug holds more than this vase?" (You could pour from one to another.) *"Is there another way to do that?"* (Measure amounts with cupfuls.)
◆ *"If I wanted to find out how much water there is in this fish tank, would it be best to measure how much with a bucket, or with a teaspoon?"*

◆ Starting point: whole class

◆ Have a variety of paper fish of various colours and lengths, some short and fat, others long and curved/zig-zag and so on. Compare two fish at a time. *"Is this one longer or shorter than this one? Is this little one longer or shorter than your hand? Caven, come and find a fish that is longer than your arm. How can we compare Caven's arm and the fish?"* Show how to find a fish that is about as long as someone's foot.
◆ Show how to measure a fish with a line of cubes. Point out that cubes must touch each other and be in a straight line. Let each child find out how long their shoe is with a line of cubes.
◆ Show how to measure a zig-zag fish with string.
◆ *"Without moving those fish, so you can't put them next to each other, how could we find out which one is shorter?"* (Using a stick, mark the length of one and then hold the stick next to the other fish.)

◆ Group activities

  Focus group

Compare heights in the group just by standing next to each other. Talk about 'tall' and 'short'. Stick some sheets of newspaper together, one for each pair, and ask the children to make a fish that is longer than their height.

  Teacher-independent groups

Use the photocopiable activity sheets.

Activity sheet 1: Make sure these children understand 'longer' and 'shorter' and draw attention to the two spaces their fish must fit into.

Measuring

Activity sheet 2: Provide cubes and read the task to the children. Using stick glue is best as it doesn't get on to the cubes.

Activity sheet 3: Provide cubes, newspaper, scissors and stick glue.

✦ Plenary session

✦ Check that the fish fit into their spaces. Ask group 1 if their fish is longer than their shoe. Talk about the tiny fish and how long it is in relation to two cubes and to their little finger.

✦ Let group 2 talk about the length of their shoe in cubes and the length of their longer fish. *"What else could you measure your fish with?"* (A ruler, drinking straws and so on.)
✦ *"Which is the longest/shortest fish we have? Maybe you could make an even shorter one this afternoon."*
✦ Check the measuring done by group 3 and ask them to measure the longest fish in the room with cubes or some larger unit of measurement, such as drinking straws.
✦ *"What did you enjoy doing in maths today?"*
✦ *"Maybe at home you could make an even longer fish."*

LESSON TWO MEASURING PROBLEMS

✦ Assessment focus

Can the children solve simple word problems involving length, mass or capacity, explaining how the problem was solved?

✦ Resources

✦ various sizes of boxes/packets (of fish and shark food) filled with newspaper and taped up (have at least one small heavy one and a large light one)
✦ various bottles, jugs and other containers
✦ lots of yoghurt pots
✦ matchboxes filled with sand and taped up

✦ Oral work and mental calculation

Counting cupfuls

✦ You need lots of yoghurt pots all the same size, two different-sized jugs a large bottle of water. Fill one jug with water and ask the children whether they think all the water from this jug will go into the other jug. Let them give reasons for what they say, then test it out. Decide which jug holds the

most, then let them make estimates of how many yoghurt pots you could fill from each of the jugs. Record some of the estimates, then test them out and record the number of pots. You can make a graph with cubes of these results and also do some comparing of numbers, for example *"The red jug filled 7 pots and the white jug filled 5. How many more pots did the red jug fill? What is the difference between 5 and 7?"*

✦ Starting point: whole class

✦ Ask the children to feel the weight of about four packets. Ask which is the heaviest, lightest and so on and see if they can put them in order of weight just by feeling them. (Make sure the heaviest one isn't the largest and the lightest isn't the smallest.) Ask how you can find out if you are right. Talk about different kinds of scales and what they are for.
✦ Compare the packets on balance scales and let the children talk about their estimates. Put the packets in order.
✦ You can introduce balancing parcels with some suitable units, such as 50g masses or matchboxes filled with sand.

Measuring

◆ Group activities

Focus group

Give simple weighing or other measuring problems to suit the experiences of the children, for example *"Is this packet heavier than your shoe?"* Make sure they understand that the side that goes down on a balance is the heavier. You can also assess their understanding of other measuring words, such as 'full', 'about half full', 'lightest', 'heavier than that one' and so on.

Teacher independent groups

Group 1: Ask this group to estimate first how many bucketfuls of water there are in the sink/fish tank. How could they find out?

Group 2: Ask this group to estimate and then find out whether it is further from your chair to the door, or from the sink to the door. How could they find out? Give them freedom to choose how they do the measuring, letting them select from paces, string, drinking straws and so on.

Group 3: Give one beaker and a jug to each pair of children. Ask them to estimate and then find out how many jugfuls of water they would need to give everyone in the class a beakerful of water.

◆ Plenary session

◆ Talk about how the problems were solved. Ask the children to tell you how they worked things out, for example *"You can fill five beakers from one jug, so we counted on our fingers in 5s: 5, 10, 15, 20, 25, 30. So we need six jugfuls and a bit more to make 32."*
◆ *"There were six garden canes from the chair to the door, but we needed ten canes from the sink so the sink is further."*
◆ *"We knew this one was heavier than that one, so this one must be the lightest."*
◆ *"Someone tell me what estimating means."*
◆ *"What kinds of things can you measure with rulers?"*
◆ *"Why are balance scales no use for working out how tall you are?"*

◆ Further activities

◆ During PE, measure with paces and 'pigeon steps' (putting one foot directly on the toe of the previous foot). *"The mat is 9 of Ellie's pigeon steps across but only 6 of mine. Why is that?"* (Establish that your feet are bigger.)
◆ Estimate in many different contexts, guessing measures and numbers, for example *"How many strides across our carpet?"* or *"How many children on that PE mat?"* or *"About how many children/teachers are there in our school?"*

◆ Extension

◆ Make two sea worms, one half the length of the other.
◆ How tall are you in cubes?

◆ Support

◆ Give plenty of structured play using a wide variety of measuring equipment, for example making a teddy bears' tea party with drinks for ten teddies and play-dough sandwiches.

✦ How big are the fish? ✦

✦ Make a paper 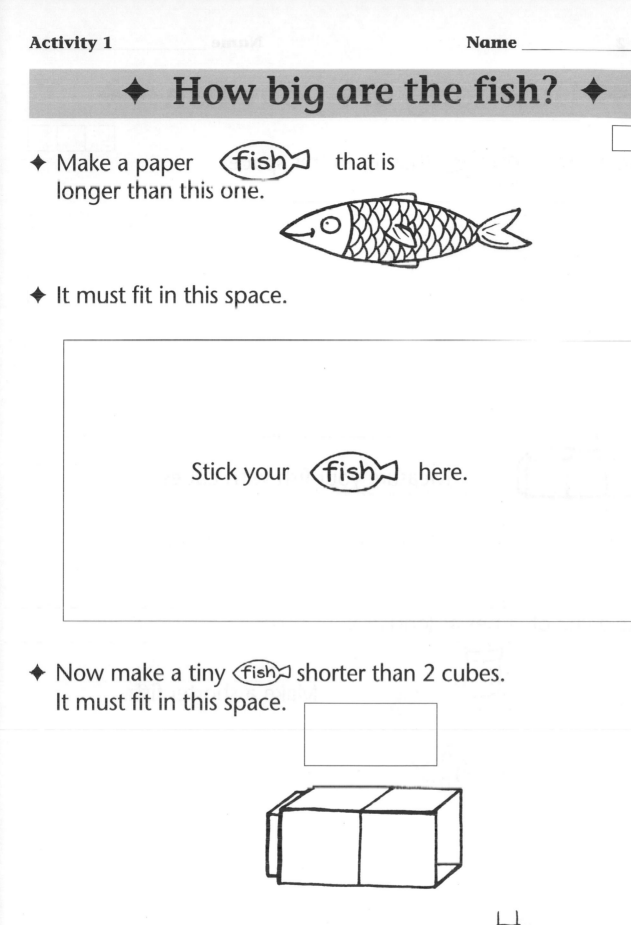 fish that is longer than this one.

✦ It must fit in this space.

> Stick your fish here.

✦ Now make a tiny fish shorter than 2 cubes. It must fit in this space.

📖 Make a fish longer than your shoe.

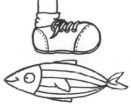

✦ How long are your fish? ✦

✦ Make a long (fish) that fits in this space.

Measure your fish with cubes.

My fish is ☐ cubes long.

✦ Make a line of cubes as long as your shoe.

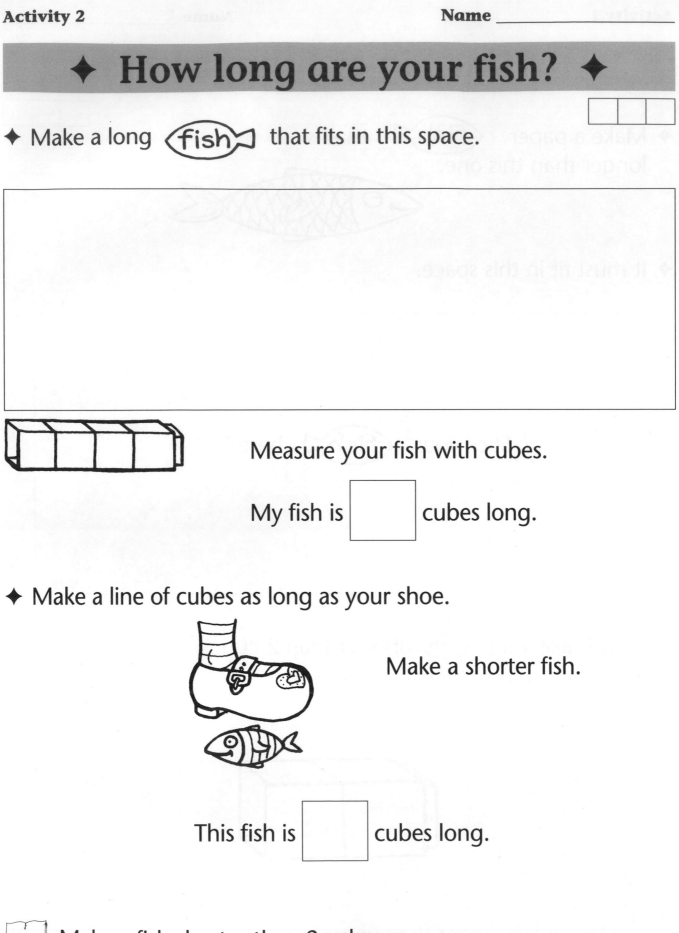

Make a shorter fish.

This fish is ☐ cubes long.

Make a fish shorter than 2 cubes.

✦ How long are your fish? ✦

✦ Make 3 〈fish〉

Make a long one to fit in this space.

The long fish is about ☐ cubes long.

Make a shorter one for this space.

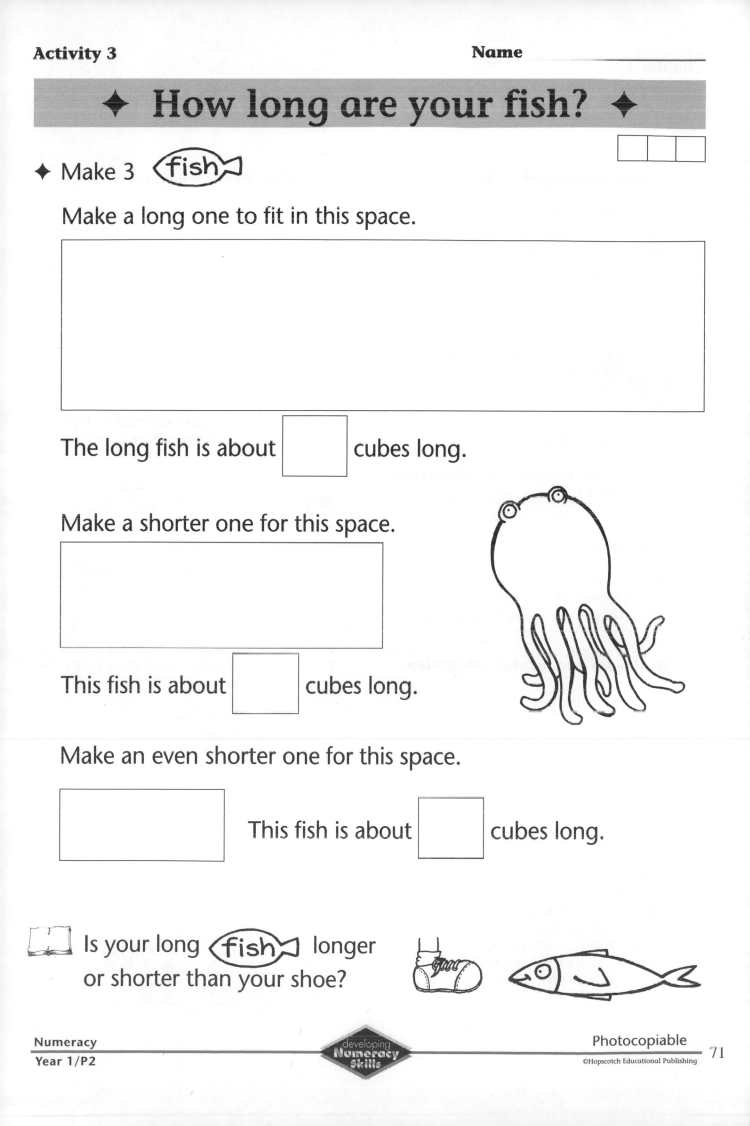

This fish is about ☐ cubes long.

Make an even shorter one for this space.

This fish is about ☐ cubes long.

Is your long 〈fish〉 longer
or shorter than your shoe?

Sorting and organising

◆ Overall learning objectives

◆ Solve a problem by collecting, sorting and organising information.
◆ Sort using a simple tree sorting diagram.
◆ Count and compare numbers in sets.
◆ Represent numbers with cubes and pictures and answer questions about those representations.
◆ With support, make a simple pictogram.

◆ LESSON ONE SORTING SEA CREATURES

◆ Assessment focus

Can the children solve a problem by collecting and sorting information?

◆ Resources

◆ a variety (about six) of pre-made, different kinds of paper sea creatures (spotty, long and thin, starfish, crabs and so on – see the activity sheets)

◆ Oral work and mental calculation

Counting and making sets

◆ *"Stand up all the children who have black shoes. How many? (Sometimes count in 2s, 5s and 10s.) Do you think more people have brown shoes or black shoes?"*
◆ *"Everyone take a coin from the pot. Stand over here if you have a 1p coin. How many of you are there with 1p?"* (and so on)
◆ Make sets and count them, for example for how you come to school, favourite stories (from a choice of about five), hair colour, shoe size, numbers of brothers and sisters, who likes porridge and who doesn't.
◆ Ask questions about the data, for example *"How many more children like white bread than like brown?"*
◆ Find simple problems to solve, such as *"What time do most people go to bed?" "What could we do to find the answer?"*

◆ Starting point: whole class

◆ Sort the paper sea creatures into types, for example: long, thin fish; creatures with legs, sorted into five and six legs; angel fish; spotty fish. Talk about what to do with a long, thin fish that is also spotty. (You could put all the spotty fish together in their own tank if the children need a simpler task.)
◆ Put three large pieces of different-coloured paper on the floor in the middle of the circle to represent three different fish tanks. Let the children put fish they have made into one of the tanks so that each tank has a variety.
◆ Using just one of the tanks, construct a simple list or block graph, representing different fish with cubes, for example:

long thin fish	□ □ □ □
crabs	□
star fish	□ □
angel fish	□ □ □ □ □

◆ Ask questions about the graph. *"How many more angel fish than crabs? Which fish is there most of? Which one is there least of? Are there any kinds of our creatures not in this tank at all?"*

◆ Group activities

Focus group

These children collect data and work with you to construct either a table, graph or pictogram. Do this with something they suggest, or choose something simple, such as favourite colours from a choice of four. Make each 'picture' on the pictogram very simple, such as a stick person.

like red best	🧍🧍🧍🧍
like blue best	🧍🧍

72
©Hopscotch Educational Publishing

developing
Numeracy
Skills

Numeracy
Year 1/P2

Sorting and organising

 Teacher-independent groups

Group 1: Provide a bundle of different paper sea creatures and ask these children to sort them into groups, in any way they want.

Group 2: Give these children one of the tanks from the starter activity and ask them to make a block graph with cubes, or a list or table.

Group 3: These children can do the same as group 2 but with more creatures, or let them collect data of their own choice. It can help to provide class lists and let them record what they find out in their own way.

 **Plenary session**

✦ Show the pictogram from the focus group and ask questions, such as *"Which is the most popular colour?" "How many more people like blue than like yellow?" "Do you think you would get the same results if you ask class 4 as well?"*
✦ Let the children explain their reasoning for their sorting and ask questions about graphs, such as *"How many sea creatures altogether in your tank?"*
✦ *"Tell me what you did today to solve problems."*
✦ *"What was the most interesting thing you did today in maths?"*

LESSON TWO
TREE DIAGRAMS

Assessment focus

Can the children sort using a simple tree sorting diagram?

Resources

✦ Unifix cubes
✦ number cards
✦ Blu-tack
✦ paper fish tanks
✦ scissors and stick glue

Oral work and mental calculation

Calculating more/fewer and finding difference

✦ Children often find the 'difference between' two numbers confusing. Spend time comparing ages. *"Dan is 6 and his sister is 8. The difference is 2 years."* With trains of 6 and 8 cubes show how 6 cubes match each other and 2 are left over.
✦ Use a wide range of numbers, linking these to

graphs around the class and to numbers of children. *"16 children walk to school and 19 don't walk. What is more, 16 or 19? How many more?"*
✦ Using number cards to 10 (later, 20), two children turn over a card each and everyone tries to work out the difference.

Starting point: whole class

✦ Do the activity as described on Activity sheet 2. Write out the questions (*"Does it have legs?"* and so on) and place these on the carpet (or on a wall with Blu-tack) with paper 'roads' to the next question, and four paper fish tanks at the end of the roads. Use the appropriate four sea creatures and ask the children the first question. Let them take the two with legs along the road to the next question and another child take the two without legs to *"Is it long and thin?"* Give them plenty of time to think about what is going on and ask them for their reasoning at each stage.
✦ When the creatures are in their four tanks ask some other children to repeat the activity, giving another chance to read the questions, as this is needed for the activity sheets. Leave this whole-class version up to help the children complete their sheets, and for an interactive display.

Sorting and organising

◆ Group activities

Focus group

Set up another sorting tree. You could do this with plastic sorting toys, (Does it have wheels? Does it go on water? and so on) or with coins (Is it silver? Is it round? Does it have more than one colour?) or with shapes ('Is it round? Does it have 6 flat faces?').

Teacher-independent groups

Use the photocopiable activity sheets.

Activity sheet 1: Provide scissors and stick glue. The task can be completed just by matching the cut-out fish, but it would help to read the words as well to clarify the task. The children cut out their creatures (or draw them) and place them in the right tank. They can draw more and count them.

Activity sheet 2: This activity is a repeat of the whole-class starter, so the children should be able to complete it independently. You could ask them to show you where they have put their fish before they stick them.

Activity sheet 3: Make sure that these children can read the questions. This sorting diagram has one more creature than the starter activity.

◆ Plenary session

◆ Ask the children to give you their reasons for how they have sorted things. *"Why did you put it there and not in this tank? Tell me how you know you are right."*
◆ The focus group can show their sorting tree and give reasons for what they did. Encourage the others to ask them questions.
◆ *"What did you enjoy in maths today?"*
◆ *"Tell me something you have learned about solving problems."*

◆ Further activities

◆ Give the children more experience with collecting their own data. Try to make this about something real, for example plan an activity such as an afternoon of races, giving each child a drink that they like. *"Which two drinks are the most popular?"*

◆ Extension

◆ Do other pictograms, for example showing favourite stories from a choice of about five. The pictures could be books, such as in the example opposite.

◆ Support

◆ Make simple block graphs with cubes.
◆ Make simple lists and tables, for example of favourite television programmes.

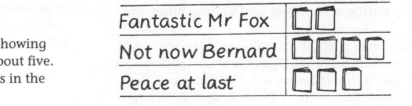

Fantastic Mr Fox	☐☐
Not now Bernard	☐☐☐☐
Peace at last	☐☐☐

74

Numeracy
Year 1/P2

◆ Spots and legs ◆

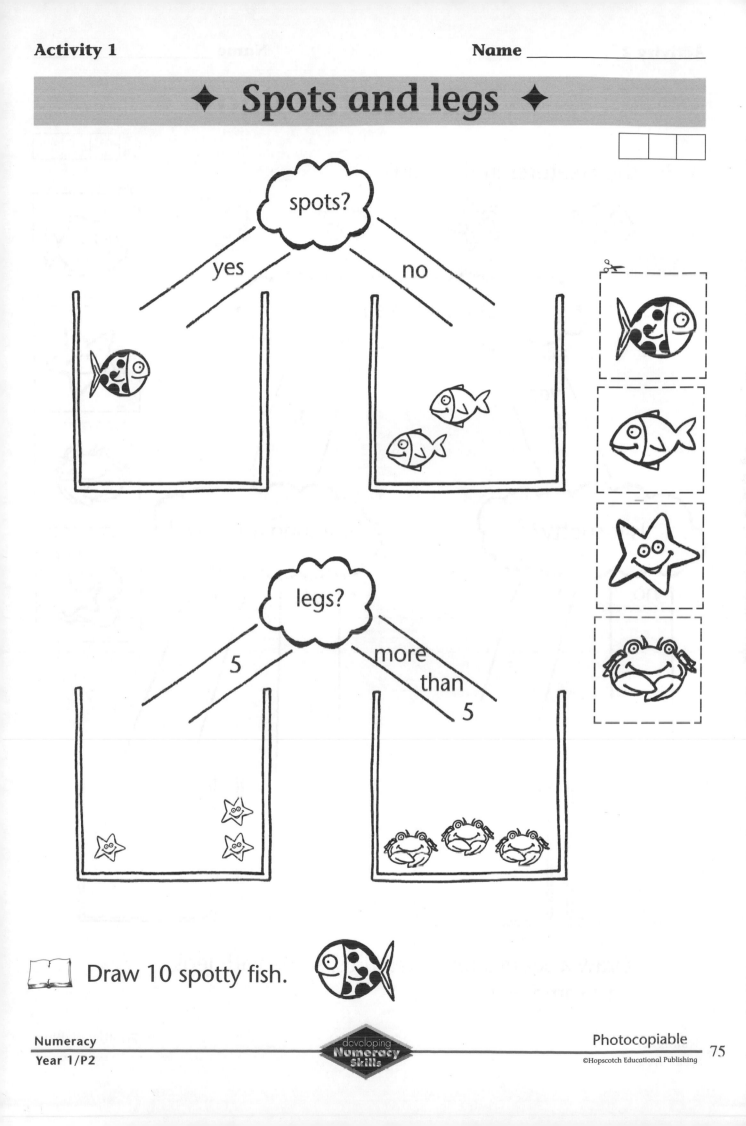

spots?

yes   no

legs?

5   more than 5

📖 Draw 10 spotty fish.

                    Photocopiable
©Hopscotch Educational Publishing   75

◆ **Where do they go?** ◆

✦ Put the creatures in their tanks.

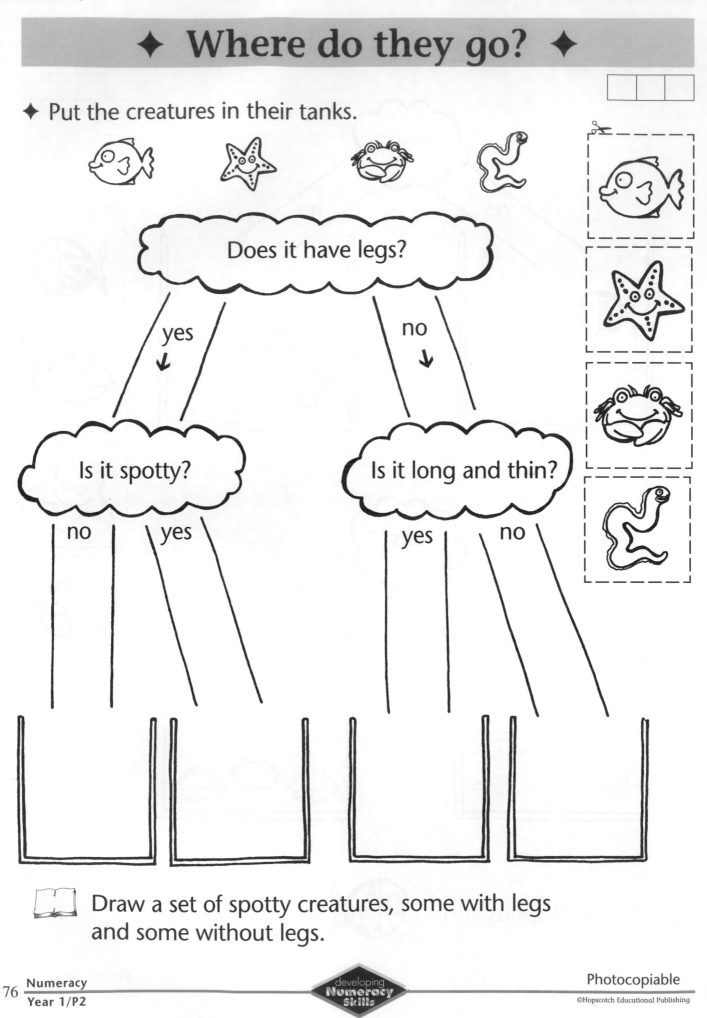

Draw a set of spotty creatures, some with legs and some without legs.

Shape and space

◆ Overall learning objectives

- ✦ Solve mathematical problems or puzzles and explain reasoning.
- ✦ Describe and classify common 3D and 2D shapes according to their properties.
- ✦ Use 3D shapes to make models.
- ✦ Use 2D shapes to make patterns.
- ✦ Make halves of paper shapes.

◆ LESSON ONE 2D SHAPES

◆ Assessment focus

Can the children use 2D shapes to make patterns and solve mathematical problems or puzzles and explain their reasoning?

◆ Resources

- ✦ lots of paper squares about 10cm, rectangles 10cm by 20cm, circles 10cm across, equilateral triangles with 10cm edges (if you provide card templates of these, the children can make more)
- ✦ thick crayons

◆ Oral work and mental calculation

Number bonds to 5/10/20

- ✦ Use two sets of number cards 0–5 or 0–10 or above and place them in the centre of the circle face down. Choose a target number (5 with cards 0–5, 8 or 10 with cards 0–10, 15 or 20 with cards 0–20). Go around the circle, each child turning over two cards and adding them. If they add up to the target number, that child keeps those cards. The children must try to remember where cards are placed to make the numbers. They score 10 for each card they hold at the end. Play the game in smaller groups, with two sets of cards for each group.

◆ Starting point: whole class

This is a long lesson best done over two or three days.

- ✦ Talk about the paper shapes: which ones have three straight edges; the two with four straight edges and how they are different; circles with round edges. Each child should take a shape and fold it in half. Look at the results of this and the different ways to fold squares and rectangles in half.
- ✦ The children can then colour half of the shapes, using one of just two colours (this makes more effective displays), but only using one colour on each shape.

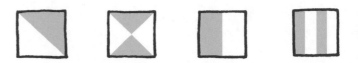

- ✦ Now, or on another day, do the group activities. Group 1 children should use just the shapes with four sides (already coloured in half), group 2 uses just squares and group 3 uses triangles, circles and squares. (This would be more straightforward if done with uncoloured paper shapes.)

◆ Group activities

 Focus group

Work with this group either to find more ways to fold and colour a square in half or work with them to do the same activity as group 3.

 Teacher-independent groups

Group 1: Using squares and rectangles, this group should make a patchwork quilt. Point out that they could stick two squares together to make a rectangle.

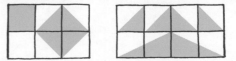

Group 2: This group should make a patchwork quilt just with squares, but they can only use squares coloured in one of the colours. They should try to make shapes that match each other, or that make

developing **Numeracy Skills**

Shape and space

other patterns and make more folded and coloured squares so that the pattern works. Suggest that they try them out before sticking them on.

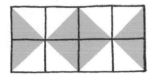

Group 3: The children should work in pairs to make a picture with just one of the three shapes in each row, but each row must be different. There are six possible rows (see opposite).

◆ Plenary session

✦ Each group can show their patterns. Draw out points about halves, for example how group 1's rectangles are twice as long as the squares. Talk about the fact that there are lots of ways to arrange these.

✦ Look at the patterns created on the group 2 quilt. (Have some spare squares to demonstrate and to let other children try to copy the patterns.)
✦ Look at the group 3 picture and decide if each row is different.
✦ *"What did you learn today about shapes?"*

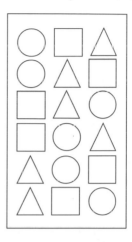

LESSON TWO
3D SHAPES

◆ Assessment focus

Can the children talk about the properties of 3D shapes and use them to make models?

◆ Resources

✦ number cards; 'greater than', 'less than' cards
✦ 3D shapes
✦ hoops, feely bags
✦ cards with the names of shapes on them

◆ Oral work and mental calculation

Greater than/less than

✦ Put four pieces of paper on the floor with a 'greater than' (>) or 'less than' (<) sign between them.
✦ Choose children to take a card each from a face-down pack of 0–9. They must decide how to lay

the cards on the pieces of paper so that the number sentence is true, for example '82 is greater than 57'.

✦ Then play in fours. Give each pair two cards and ask them to try to make a number greater than the pair next to them.

◆ Starting point: whole class

✦ Sort a set of 3D shapes into groups with large hoops, for example those with flat faces and those with curved faces. (The cone and cylinder will need to be in both sets, so overlap the hoops.) Try out shapes to see if they will roll down a slope. Count the six flat faces of a cube and cuboid and talk about the differences in the sizes of the faces.

✦ Fun with shapes ✦

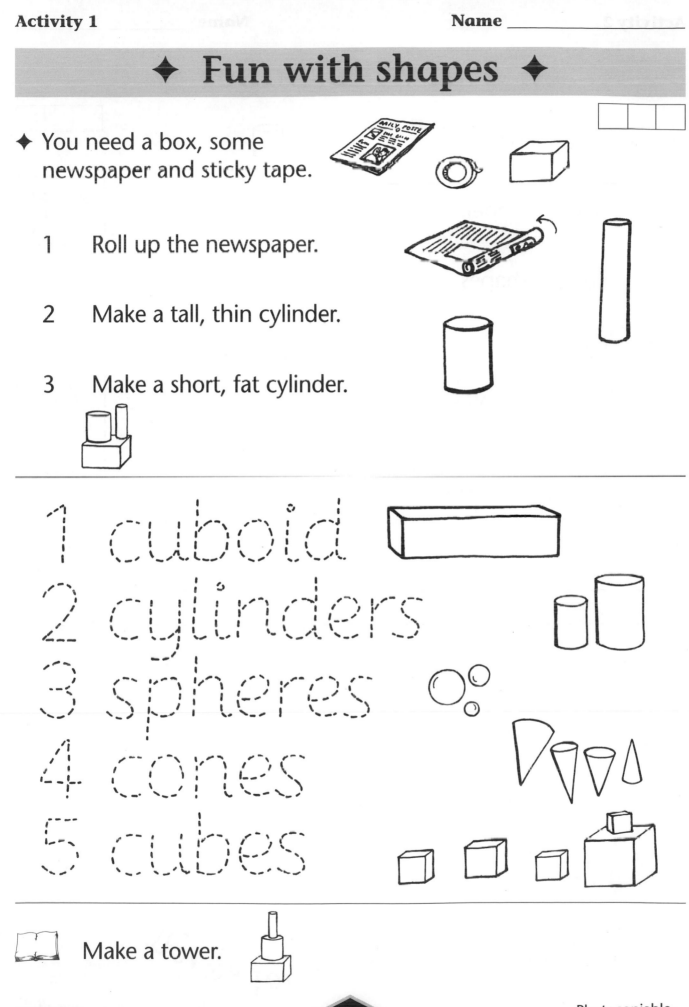

✦ You need a box, some
newspaper and sticky tape.

1   Roll up the newspaper.

2   Make a tall, thin cylinder.

3   Make a short, fat cylinder.

1 cuboid
2 cylinders
3 spheres
4 cones
5 cubes

Make a tower.

✦ Fun with shapes ✦

✦ Use these shapes.

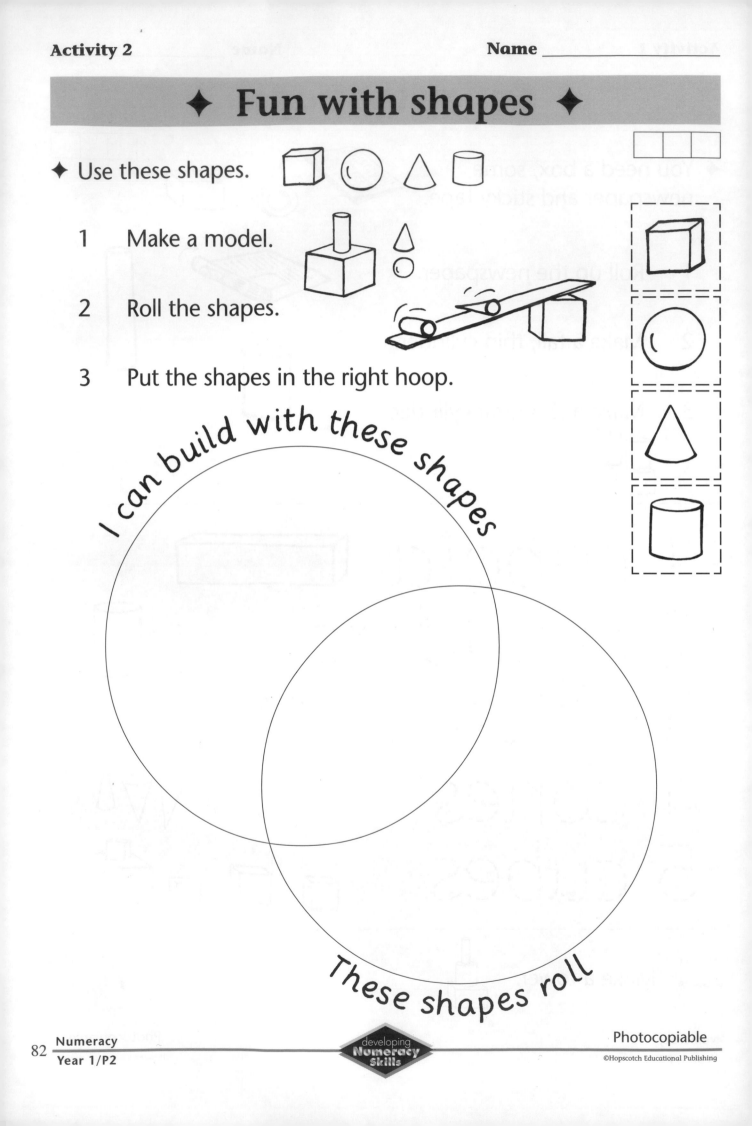

1   Make a model.

2   Roll the shapes.

3   Put the shapes in the right hoop.

I can build with these shapes

These shapes roll

◆ Fun with shapes ◆

◆ You need paper, sticky tape,
Polydrons and play dough.

	Polydrons	paper	play dough
I can make 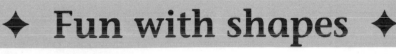 with	✔		
○			
△			
▭			
△			

Make a model
with flat faces.

What can you
do with
curved faces?

Position, direction and movement

◆ Overall learning objectives

✦ Use everyday language to describe position, direction and movement.
✦ Give instructions for moving in straight lines and round corners.
✦ Talk about turns, left and right.

LESSON ONE
WHERE IS IT?

◆ Assessment focus

Can the children follow instructions and understand the language of position?

◆ Resources

✦ a special seashell
✦ a box
✦ cards with words for position, ('in,' 'beside,' 'underneath' and so on)
✦ 2D shapes
✦ large pieces of paper
✦ large books or folders
✦ Lego, Polydrons, bricks

◆ Oral work and mental calculation

Mixed mental calculations

✦ *"How could you work out 5 + 6? Did someone do it another way? How could you do 3 plus 15?"* (Remind the children that it is easier to start with the largest number first.) *"Can you double/halve these numbers? 2, 6, 12."* Keep adding 10 to 5, 15, 25, 35 and so on. Add 9 to single-digit numbers, for example 3 + 10 is 13 so 3 + 9 must be 12. *"Give me a multiple of 2/5/10. Give me a multiple of 5 that is less than/more than 15/50. What do multiples of 2/5/10 end in? Let's count in 3s using our fingers. When I add 3 to my number I get 11. What is my number? Tell me a number that is larger than 20 and is an even number."*

◆ Starting point: whole class

✦ *"Today you are going to learn about lots of different words for where we put things. Look at this special seashell."* (Place it on top of or in a box.) *"Where is the shell?"* Then give instructions to the children for where to put the shell, for example *under* the table, *to the left* of Sophie and so on. One child chooses the relevant word cards and makes a sentence, such as 'the shell is *opposite* Abdul.'

✦ Demonstrate giving instructions, placing 2D shapes on a piece of paper. Ask six confident children to sit with their backs to you (or you can sit behind a big book) and they put their paper in front of them. Give instructions such as *"Put your paper so that the long edge is at the bottom. Put your square half way along this bottom edge so that one edge of the square is on the edge of the paper. Now put your yellow triangle on the left hand end of your paper, touching the bottom and the side."*

◆ Group activities

 Focus group

Choose parts of the starter activity to suit the group. They can work in pairs, or you can give the instructions.

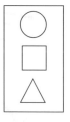

"Put the circle above the square and the triangle under the square."

 Teacher-independent groups

Group 1: Working in pairs, give each pair about four Lego bricks (an identical set, all the same size but more than one colour). They take it in turns to instruct their partner to make a tower. If this is too hard, let the pairs just make identical towers, but in full view of each other, selecting one child to be the leader for half the time, then change over.

Position, direction and movement

Group 2: These children take about three Polydrons each (an identical set) and take turns to give each other instructions from behind a big book, for example *"Join the red square on to the blue triangle. Put it so the triangle is at the top."* and so on.

Group 3: These children should do the same as group 2 but using a wider variety of shapes.

✦ Plenary session

✦ *"What do you need to do when someone is giving you instructions?"* (Listen very carefully.) *"Tell me some of the words you used when you gave instructions."* Sort out words that were used and words that weren't and therefore might need practising again (by hiding the shell as in the whole-class starter activity).

✦ Let the children show how their constructions are the same (or not!). Listen to problems that they had.

✦ *"Did anyone learn a new word today?"*

LESSON TWO
MAZES

✦ Assessment focus

Can the children use everyday language to describe direction and movement, including turns and (later) left and right?

✦ Resources

✦ number cards
✦ number line
✦ washing line and pegs
✦ see-through containers
✦ floor robot (if possible)
✦ boxes or class furniture

✦ Oral work and mental calculation

Ordering numbers and identifying a number between two others

✦ Place number cards 0–20 or 0–100 (or a selection of these) face down on the carpet. Go around the circle, three children at a time picking up a card

each. They look at their numbers and decide who has the largest, who has the smallest and who has the number that lies in between. (Relate this to the number line.) The child with the number between keeps their card and the other two numbers are put out of play. Once you have gone all the way around the circle, see who has the largest and smallest 'between' numbers. Put these at each end of a washing line and order all the 'between' cards on the line between those two numbers. Vary the game by focusing on the largest or the smallest numbers. Or just two children pick up cards and they have to say a number between those two.

✦ Starting point: whole class

✦ The ideal introduction to this work is a floor robot. Set up a simple maze on the carpet with some boxes and ask the children to make the robot go through the maze using instructions: forward, back, left and right. If you don't have a robot, make a maze with chairs and let the class direct a child through it by giving instructions. (With a very confident child you could suggest they try doing this blind-folded.)

Position, direction and movement

✦ Note who is good with spatial work. (Children who struggle with number can sometimes be good at spatial ideas and, conversely, those who usually work with group 3 for number may have orientation problems, so take care when allocating activity sheets.)

✦ Group activities

Focus group

Give this group more experience with the floor robot. Or, pairs can use a large board to make a road for toy cars or play people, using bricks/Lego/Polydrons. Alternatively they can draw one on a large piece of paper. Assess carefully who can talk about forward, back, turn left, turn right.

Teacher-independent groups

Use the photocopiable activity sheets.

Activity sheet 1: This simple maze has two routes through it and the children should draw these in two different colours. As an extra task, ask them to find the five tiny seashells and be ready to tell you where they are.

Activity sheet 2: This maze is more complex and has two routes, starting from the bottom, so they both start off going forward. Ask the children to note where they turn left and where they turn right. These turns to be to the *children's* left and right.

Activity sheet 3: (This activity is only suitable for children who have had floor robot or Logo experience.) This maze starts at the top, so they must make their turns left and right, not as their left and right, but the *robot's left and right*. The turns are right angles ('right 90' with Logo). There is only one route through.

✦ Plenary session

✦ Ask the group 1 children to show how they get through their maze, following their route with their finger. Use descriptions by individuals of how they get from one tiny shell to the next to assess language.
✦ The focus group can introduce their road and leave it where others can play with it.
✦ Groups 2 and 3 children should describe their routes. *"Where did you need to go back/forward/turn left/right?"*

✦ Further activities

✦ Make patterns with shapes, including repeating patterns and symmetrical ones.
✦ Ask the children to tell you exactly how to get from their class to the hall/playground and so on.
✦ In PE, practise left and right turns.

✦ Extension

✦ The children can make simple maps of journeys around the school, or their route home.

✦ Support

✦ Give as much experience with Logo and floor robots as you can.
✦ For some activities, children who confuse left and right can be helped with a red band on their right wrist.
✦ Play games that involve following directions, such as *"Everyone run to the wall on the left!"*

◆ Through the maze ◆

◆ Find 2 routes through the maze.

✦ Through the maze ✦

✦ Find 2 routes through the maze.

start

✦ Through the maze ✦

✦ Find the way through the maze.

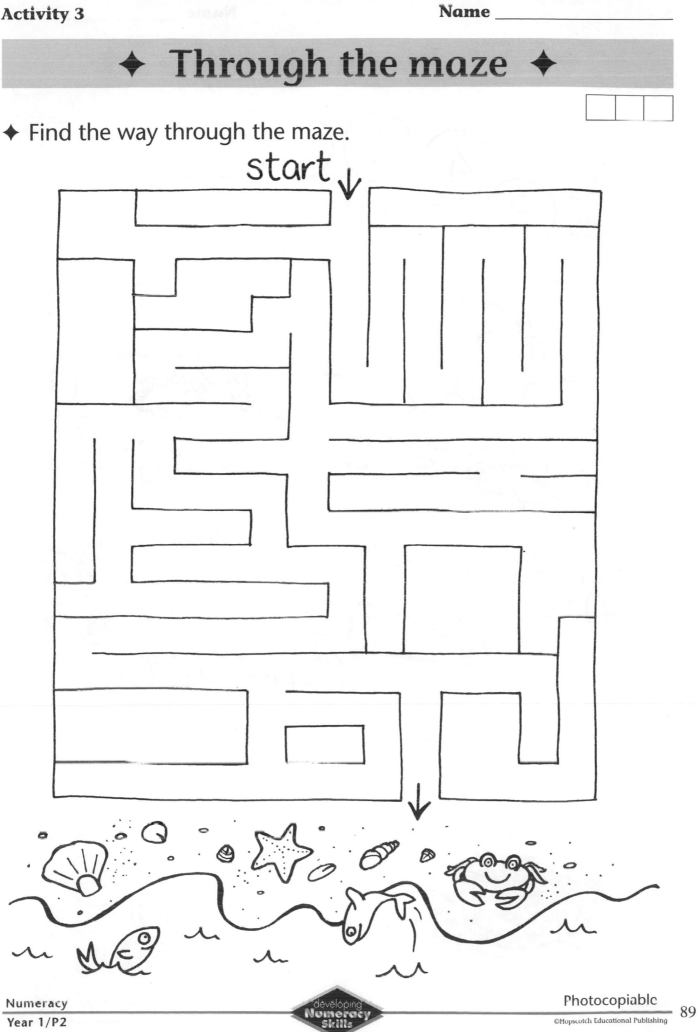

start

◆ A fishy number line ◆

developing Numeracy Skills

◆ Three in a row ◆

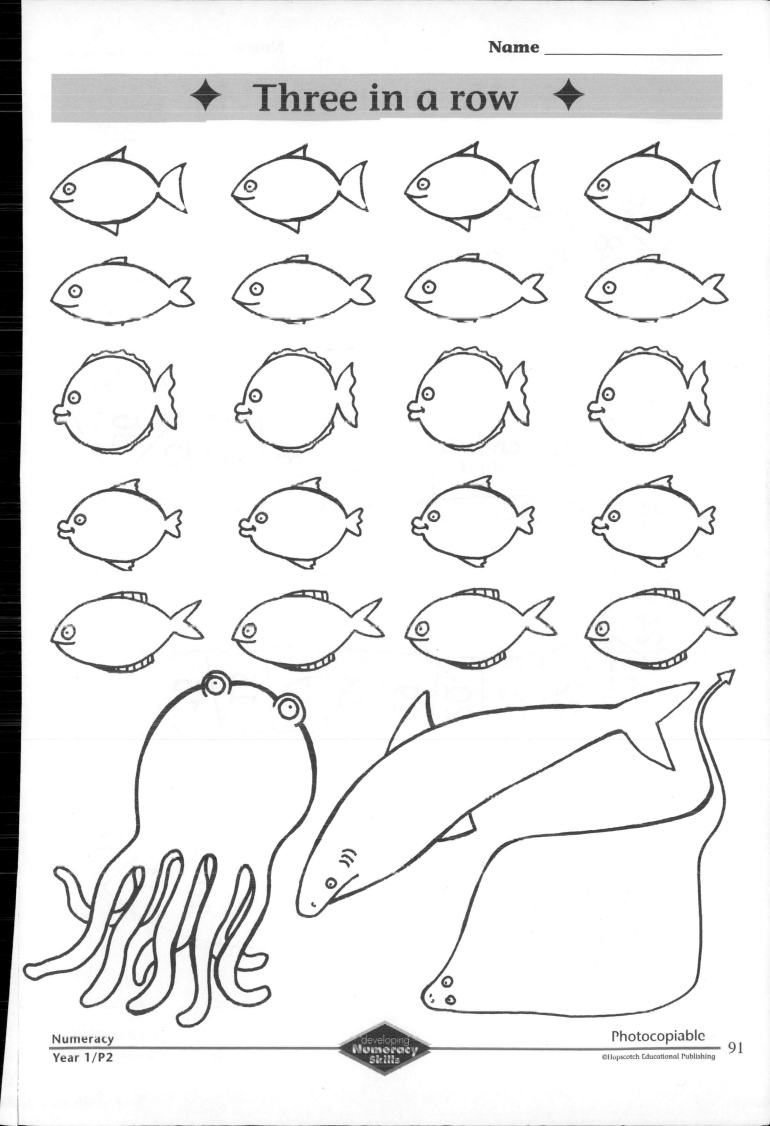

developing
Numeracy
Skills

✦ Number line ✦

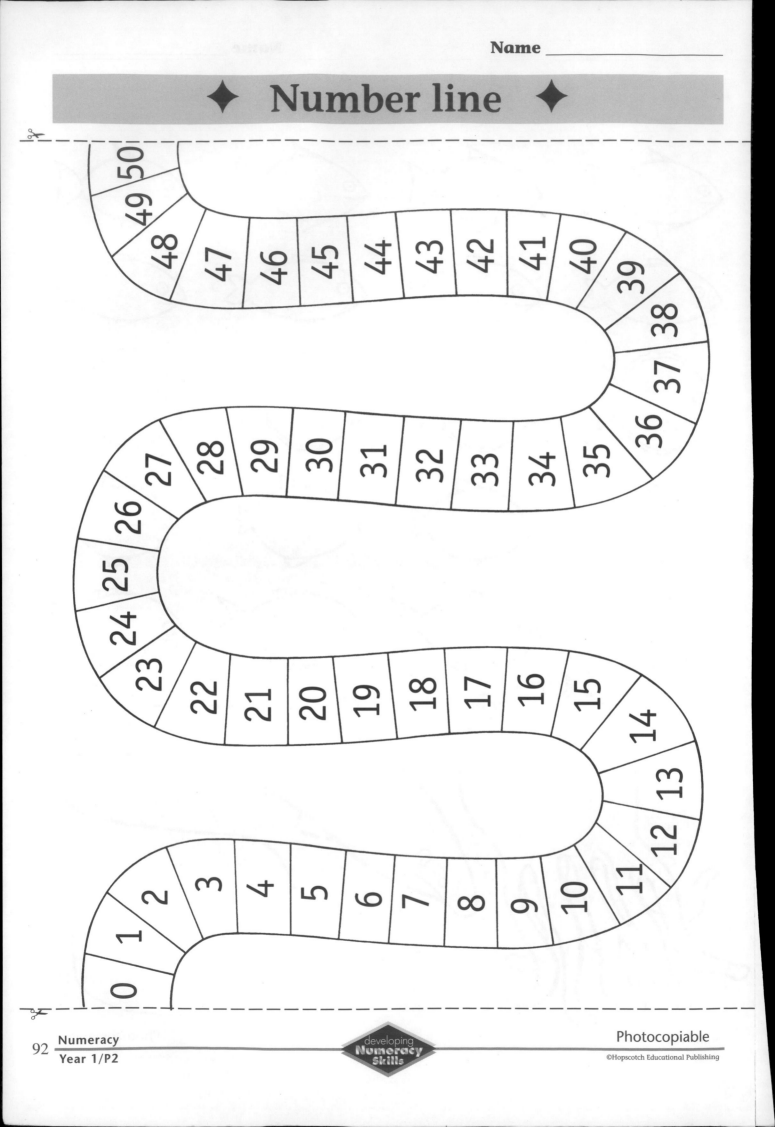

developing
Numeracy
Skills

Photocopiable

◆ Number line ◆

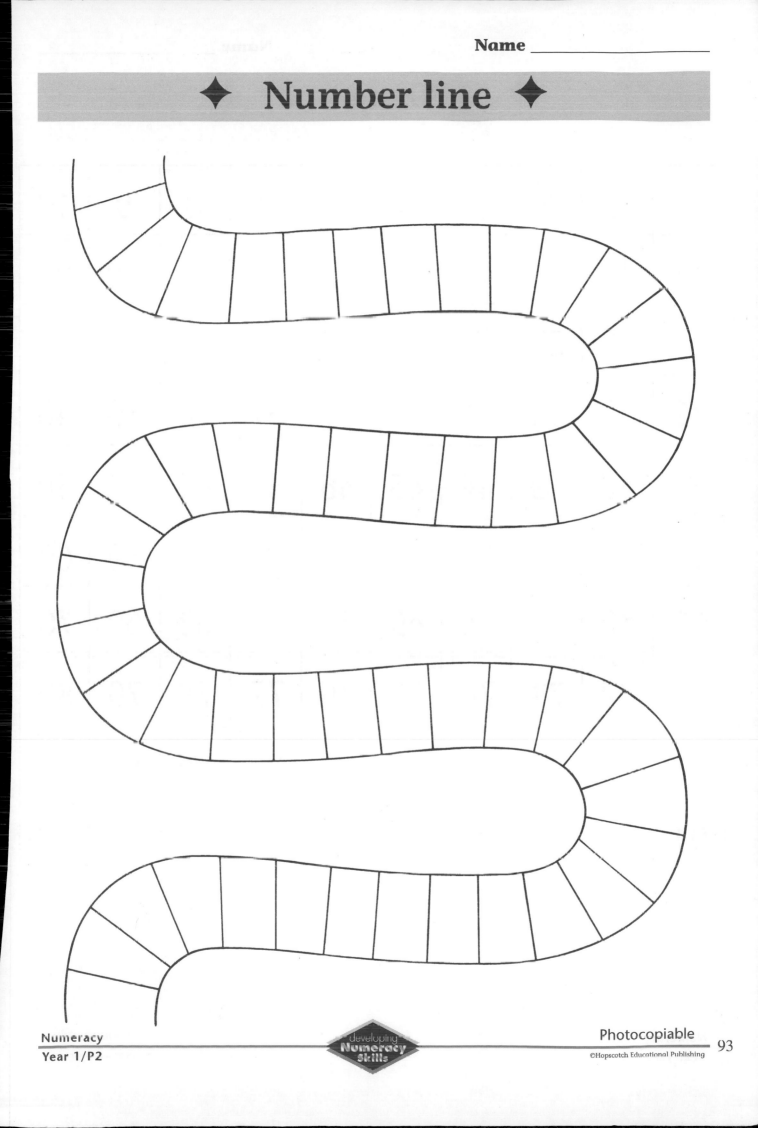

developing
**Numeracy
Skills**

✦ 100 square ✦

1	2	3	4	5	6	7	8	9	10
11	12	13	14	15	16	17	18	19	20
21	22	23	24	25	26	27	28	29	30
31	32	33	34	35	36	37	38	39	40
41	42	43	44	45	46	47	48	49	50
51	52	53	54	55	56	57	58	59	60
61	62	63	64	65	66	67	68	69	70
71	72	73	74	75	76	77	78	79	80
81	82	83	84	85	86	87	88	89	90
91	92	93	94	95	96	97	98	99	100

developing Numeracy Skills

Photocopiable

©Hopscotch Educational Publishing

◆ Assessment ◆

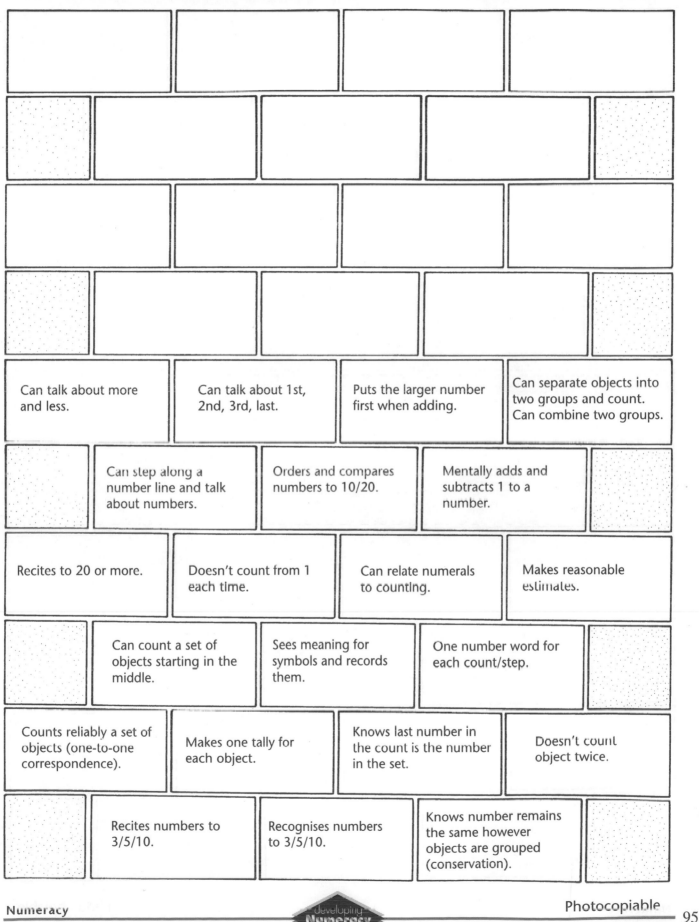

Can talk about more and less.	Can talk about 1st, 2nd, 3rd, last.	Puts the larger number first when adding.	Can separate objects into two groups and count. Can combine two groups.
	Can step along a number line and talk about numbers.	Orders and compares numbers to 10/20.	Mentally adds and subtracts 1 to a number.	
Recites to 20 or more.	Doesn't count from 1 each time.	Can relate numerals to counting.	Makes reasonable estimates.
	Can count a set of objects starting in the middle.	Sees meaning for symbols and records them.	One number word for each count/step.	
Counts reliably a set of objects (one-to-one correspondence).	Makes one tally for each object.	Knows last number in the count is the number in the set.	Doesn't count object twice.
	Recites numbers to 3/5/10.	Recognises numbers to 3/5/10.	Knows number remains the same however objects are grouped (conservation).	

©Hopscotch Educational Publishing

◆ Assessment ◆

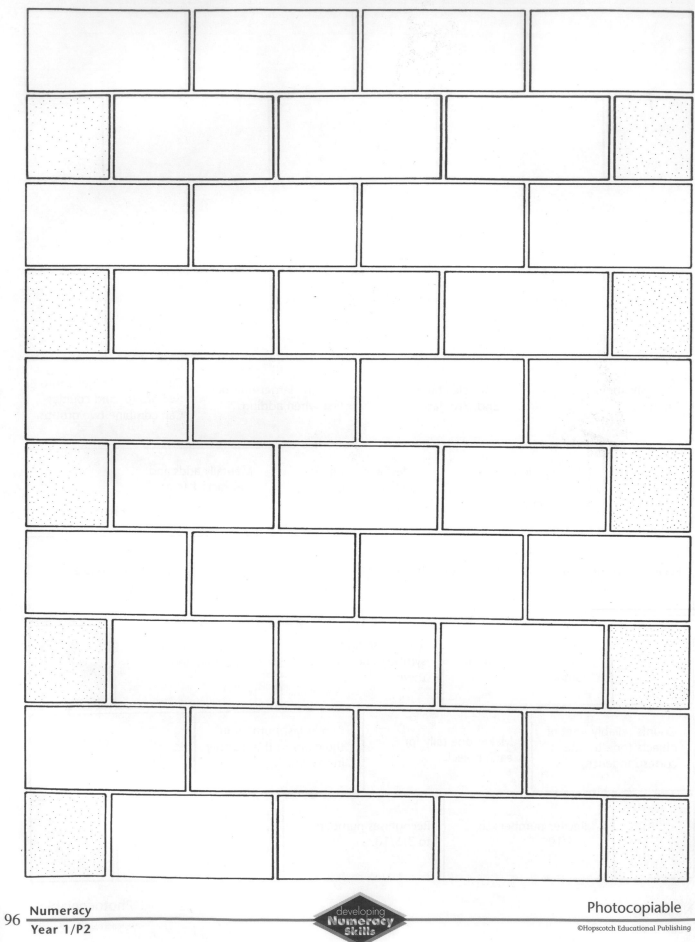

developing
**Numeracy
Skills**

Photocopiable

©Hopscotch Educational Publishing